SITE LEVELLING
FOR STUDENTS

SITE
LEVELLING
for STUDENTS

J. H. ARNISON, M.I.W.H.S., F.B.S.I., M.I.A.T., A.Inst.P.C.

Lecturer/Tutor Public Works and Highway
Courses, Riversdale Technical College, Liverpool

LONDON   ILIFFE BOOKS LTD

First published in 1968 by Iliffe Books Ltd.,
Dorset House, Stamford Street, London, S.E.1

Filmset by Photoprint Plates Ltd., Wickford, Essex
Printed in England by J. W. Arrowsmith Ltd
Bristol, 3
Bound by The Chapel River Press Ltd. Andover
Hants

CONTENTS

PREFACE

This book has been prepared mainly for students and other readers who have little, if any, knowledge of the basic requirements of levelling for construction work. The text has therefore been kept as simple as possible so that it can be easily understood.

Although the work covered is elementary and is intended mainly as a guide for those who only require knowledge of the elements of levelling as part of their duties, it will also be found invaluable to those who intend to progress into the more advanced fields of levelling and surveying.

It is hoped that those concerned with construction work will also find the contents of assistance, since much of the basic levelling on a site continues after a surveyor has produced datum pegs.

The craftsmen and technicians who need only a brief knowledge of levelling for their particular trades will nevertheless find this book suitable if, in order to progress further, they wish to become thoroughly familiar with the fundamentals of levelling.

Because of the high cost of buying levelling instruments it is often found that they are available for only short periods of time; consequently, alternative means of levelling may be necessary, especially on small sites where either qualified persons are not available or instruments cannot be obtained. Such methods are covered in this book, because in my opinion site works should not cease because some levelling cannot be performed.

Of especial interest to students is the detailed description of levelling instruments and their use, for in my experience many students find difficulty in using such instruments for the first time.

An attempt has been made to guide the reader through the early stages of site levelling and assist him in understanding how readings are booked and calculated for extended levelling.

The importance of correct levelling must be understood for excavation and construction work, because incorrect levels on a site can be costly, particularly if any construction work has already been carried out.

When mechanical plant is being used on a site the plant operator expects to be shown level pegs or sight rails that have to be adhered to, and failure to provide this guide may result in much expenditure when having to rectify faults in the excavation.

Theory alone is not enough for a full understanding of levelling and it is recommended that the reader make every effort to assist in site levelling operations.

1968   J.H.A.

ACKNOWLEDGEMENT

My sincere thanks are extended to Messrs Hilger and Watts Ltd, for providing information about the Autoset level, levelling staffs and the Cowley automatic level, and for granting permission to use the information when preparing this book.

Chapter 1

OBJECTS OF LEVELLING

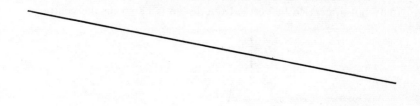

Levelling is the technique of obtaining or determining certain heights upon the earth's surface and is of paramount importance for all construction work. Without the guidance provided by *level pegs* on a site, excavation work would be haphazard and the construction work that follows could not be correctly executed.

On construction sites a *level line* is considered to be truly horizontal and is, therefore, normally suitable because of the short distances found on sites where level pegs are required.

As the earth's surface is known to be curved it follows, geometrically, that the horizontal line is tangential to the curved surface and so the greater the distance between any two level pegs the greater will be the distance from the earth's curved surface.

Because level pegs are placed at short distances and construction work on a horizontal plane does not extend any great distance without a variation in the level, it may be assumed that a *level surface* is one that is reasonably parallel to the earth's surface and corrections with regard to actual curvature will not have to be made because the surface may be stated as being horizontal to gravity.

1.1 REASONS FOR LEVELLING

Without knowledge of the technology of levelling, which is a small part of the work concerned with surveying, it would not be possible to identify height and depth. Contours which represent the rise and fall of the earth's surface indicate vertical heights above a mean level, such as *mean sea level*. By being able to determine the contours it is possible to identify very high and very low ground and this may

1

be seen clearly on an ordnance survey map by the numerals used
to indicate the relationship between contour lines and the height of
individual contours.

While certain special constructions such as retaining walls
may not appear to be vertical the design is based on the centre of

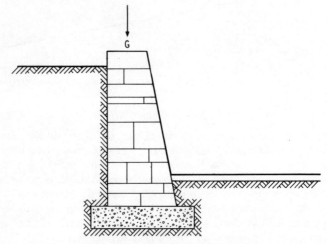

Fig. *1.1. Centre of gravity of retaining wall*

gravity (Fig. 1.1) and to enable the structure to withstand certain
stresses, etc., it will be constructed upon a level foundation.

Walls of considerable length would be built upon a series of
steps, known as a stepped foundation, to produce the required
levels or heights to which a wall has to be built. The stepped foundation is used mainly to overcome the rise or fall of the ground and to
avoid having to excavate too deeply at one end to obtain one
complete level foundation (Fig. 1.2).

Drains and sewers are laid to gradients that should provide a
self-cleansing velocity, and to reduce the number of pumping
stations for raising sewage to higher levels a pattern or series of
levels is required to provide self-cleansing velocity from one part
of the system to another.

Highways are constructed to a series of levels that will provide
gradients which permit surface water to drain from them and to
provide surfaces which are suitable to traffic. A comparison can be
seen between highways constructed prior to the twentieth century,
when in most cases the contours of the land, where used, compared
with the modern highway where more suitable gradients and

curves are used by reducing or raising the level of the highway surface.

The use of correct 'levels' on highway curves can make travelling safer and produce less wear upon surfaces.

1.2 ORDNANCE DATUM

The word *datum* may be considered as a reference mark such as the top of a manhole cover, the threshold of a doorway or a wooden peg inserted into the ground.

The ordnance datum in Great Britain, however, is a fixed datum established in relation to mean sea level at *Newlyn* in Cornwall and before that at *Liverpool* in Lancashire.

As the ordnance datum is taken as the mean sea level it is considered to have a *zero* value and shown as 0·00, so that levels on the

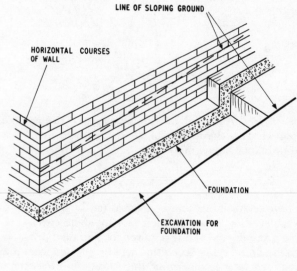

Fig. 1.2. Stepped foundation

land will be plus or minus this value according to the relationship of the land to the mean sea level.

1.3 ORDNANCE BENCH MARKS

As levels for construction work have reference to the ordnance datum, *bench marks* have been established at intervals throughout the land and are normally found on the vertical surface of permanent structures such as city halls, bridges or any structure that may be considered as permanent. In some cases a bench mark may be seen on the gatepost at entrances to estates or parks and also on some milestones.

The bench mark is cut into the surface in the shape of an arrowhead with a horizontal line superimposed upon it; the horizontal

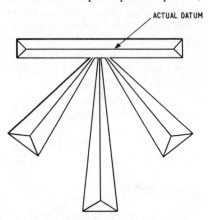

Fig. 1.3. Bench mark

line is cut as a $\overline{\wedge}$-shaped incision so that the deepest part of the incision, which is the middle of the surmounted line, indicates the actual ordnance bench mark (Fig. 1.3).

1.4 ARBITRARY DATUM

An *arbitrary datum* is one that is assumed for the purpose of providing levels or levelling on a site, such as a manhole cover, peg inserted into the ground, etc., and is required for a limited period only. This datum should be below levels that will be selected from it and when it is required later to determine the relationship between ordnance datum and the selected reduced levels this can be achieved.

If the reduced level of a peg has been taken as 50·75 on a site and later it is found that the reduced level from a bench mark is 100·25 a comparison is made of the two reduced levels.

$$
\begin{array}{rl}
100·25 & = \text{reduced level from bench mark} \\
-\ \ 50·75 & = \text{selected reduced level on the site} \\
\hline
49·50 & = \text{difference}
\end{array}
$$

Each of the reduced levels selected on the site will be increased by 49·50.

Example

Pegs selected on the site each have reduced levels as follows:

$$\text{peg A} = 50\cdot75$$
$$\text{peg B} = 50\cdot25$$
$$\text{peg C} = 49\cdot80$$

If the difference between the reduced level from the bench mark and the reduced level of peg A = 49·50, the reduced levels with reference to the bench mark will be:

$$\text{peg A} = 50\cdot75 + 49\cdot50 = 100\cdot25 \text{ R.L.}$$
$$\text{peg B} = 50\cdot25 + 49\cdot50 = 99\cdot75 \text{ R.L.}$$
$$\text{peg C} = 49\cdot80 + 49\cdot50 = 99\cdot30 \text{ R.L.}$$

1.5 GLOSSARY OF TERMS

Abney level. A small optical instrument to determine gradients.

Arbitrary datum. An assumed datum selected on a site from which level pegs may be produced.

Back sight. The first reading taken on a levelling staff after setting up the levelling instrument.

Bench mark. A permanent mark established by ordnance survey to indicate known heights above mean sea level.

Boning rods. A set of T- shaped rods each of equal length and used for establishing intermediate levels from known datums.

Camber. The section of a paved surface when the highest level is at its mid-distance.

Collimation. Referred to as the height of collimation or the line of collimation and is the sight line from the telescope of a levelling instrument to a levelling staff.

Contour line. A line, usually in brown or red colouring, used on maps to indicate points on land of equal height.

Crossfall. The difference in level between two heights on a cross-section.

Datum. A point upon a surface of known height from which reduced levels may be produced.

Diaphragm. An annular part inside the telescope of a levelling instrument.

Dumpy level. A levelling instrument consisting of a telescope and spirit level used together with a tripod and levelling staff for levelling purposes.

Even surface. Sometimes used to define a surface that has a uniform level.

Eyepiece. The viewing end of a telescope which when manipulated assists in focusing the telescope.

Fall. A given number of units differing in height between two known heights.

Flying level. A check reading made between two known levels or datums such as a bench mark and a datum on a site.

Focus. The manipulation of parts of a levelling instrument so that the object being observed may be seen clearly.

Fore sight. The last reading taken on a levelling staff before moving the levelling instrument.

Formation level. The level of a subgrade before construction work commences. Normally the level surface of excavation or fill.

Gradient. The difference in level between two heights on a longitudinal section. The amount of slope in a drain, sewer or highway.

Gradient screw. A calibrated screw on a levelling instrument used to measure gradients.

Grid. A pattern of squares set out on the land or on drawing-paper for the purpose of establishing contours.

Height of collimation. See *Collimation.*

Intermediate sight. All readings recorded between a back sight and a fore sight.

Invert. The lower part of a drain or sewer.

Level. A horizontal plane, sometimes used to determine a given height.

Level book. A specially prepared book produced for the purpose of recording readings taken by means of a levelling instrument.

Levelling. A general term used when a series of readings is being made on a site.

Levelling screws. A set of three or four screws provided at the base of a levelling instrument for the purpose of levelling the base on the tripod.

Levelling staff. A specially graduated staff used together with a levelling instrument to define readings.

Local datum. A chosen datum adjacent to a site used for the purpose of local levelling—see *Arbitrary datum.*

Mean sea level. A datum, taken at Newlyn, Cornwall, selected by ordnance survey for the purpose of establishing bench marks.

Measurement vertical. The vertical measurement established by readings produced on a levelling staff.

Object glass. A lens used in the telescope of a levelling instrument.

Ordnance survey. A survey carried out by the Ordnance Survey Department for the Government.

Parallax. The apparent motion of the cross-lines relative to the level staff. Produces errors when reading unless the eye is static. To remove parallax readjust the instrument.

Peg. A length of wood, varying from 2 in. by 2 in. to 4 in. by 4 in. section and varying in length from 18 in. to 36 in., used to establish levels or heights on a site.

Plumb bob. A weight suspended from a fine wire or cord.

Precision instrument. An instrument capable of being adjusted for a horizontal and a vertical plane.

Quick-set level. A levelling instrument with levelling screws replaced by a ball and socket, which produces a quick initial adjustment of the instrument.

Radius of curve. The distance between the arc of a curve and the centre or pivot from which it may be set out.

Reading. The observed height seen on a levelling staff when viewed through the telescope of a levelling instrument.

Reduced level. A height of any given point above a datum. The calculated level in a level book.

Rise. The amount that one point is higher than another point. When viewing through a telescope of a levelling instrument a lesser reading on the levelling staff indicates a rise of the ground, etc.

Scale. The proportion which the distance between two points on a plan bears to the horizontal distance between the same two points on the ground.

Sight line. The height of collimation.

Sight rail. A rail used as an aid on a site to determine intermediate levels between known levels.

Sopwith levelling staff. A staff graduated in feet, tenths and hundredths used together with a levelling instrument for the purpose of levelling.

Stadia lines. Additional horizontal lines above and below the main horizontal etched line or web when viewed through a telescope. Used as an aid for calculating distances.

Staff. A graduated staff used with a levelling instrument as an aid to levelling. May be a Sopwith staff, Scotch staff or similar but will be graduated.

Target bar. Used as an aid with an automatic level to determine the height of collimation.

Temporary bench mark. Sometimes referred to as a T.B.M. and indicates a fixed point or height to be used for reference on a sight.

Undulation. The rise and fall of a continuous surface.

Vertical measurement. See *Measurement vertical*.

1.6 ABBREVIATIONS OF TERMS

Certain abbreviations are sometimes used and should be understood:

B.M.	=	bench mark
M.S.L.	=	mean sea level
O.D.	=	ordnance datum
T.B.M.	=	temporary bench mark
D.P.C.	=	damp proof course
B.S.	=	back sight
I.S.	=	intermediate sight
F.S.	=	fore sight
R.L.	=	reduced level
G.L.	=	ground level
INVERT	=	invert level
R.F.	=	representative fraction
M.H.	=	manhole

Chapter 2

LEVELLING WITHOUT INSTRUMENTS

A certain amount of levelling to produce level or 'height' pegs will always have to be carried out on a site when a levelling instrument is not available or conditions do not permit the use of an instrument.

The essential equipment required for this type of levelling would be a spirit-level, straight-edge, boning rods, wooden square and an A-level.

2.1 SPIRIT-LEVEL

A spirit-level consists of an elongated container made from metal or hardwood with a bubble-tube positioned centrally in the top of the container. The spirit-levels vary in size from 3 in. length to 3 ft

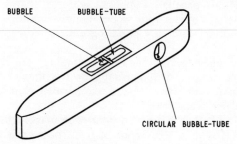

Fig. 2.1. Spirit-level

length. Those up to 9 in. length can normally be carried in a pocket while larger ones would normally be kept in a site office or in a tool-kit.

Some spirit-levels contain a bubble-tube set centrally in the length of the container and a smaller bubble-tube set near one end and sometimes referred to as the circular bubble-tube because the aperture in the container is circular in shape (Fig. 2.1).

2.2 STRAIGHT-EDGE

A straight-edge may be made from wood or steel and is not of any standard length, but for the purposes of levelling on a site a length of 4–12 ft is most suitable.

The straight-edge may consist of a length of wood 3 in. by 1 in. section to 6 in. by 1 in. section. Those over 6 ft long should have the

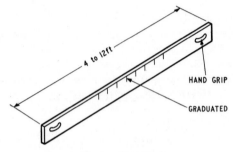

Fig. 2.2. Straight-edge

6 in. by 1 in. section. The section must be accurate throughout so that all sides are parallel to opposite sides.

Straight-edges made from wood should contain hand grips cut into them to facilitate easy handling and to reduce the possibility of warping.

Steel straight-edges, other than scraping straight-edges used for concrete surfaces, will normally be less than 8 ft long unless specially made and will consist of two parallel strips of steel joined by a perforated web of steel.

It is convenient to have a straight-edge marked through in divisions of 1 ft with sub-divisions of 6 in. or corresponding metric measurements (Fig. 2.2).

2.3 BONING RODS

Boning rods are made in sets of three and may consist of three T-shaped rods, each of equal size and shape, or two rods identical to each other and a third one consisting of a longer rod and a detachable T-piece.

The standard boning rods each being of equal size would be used for straightforward levelling where changes in the *level* surface

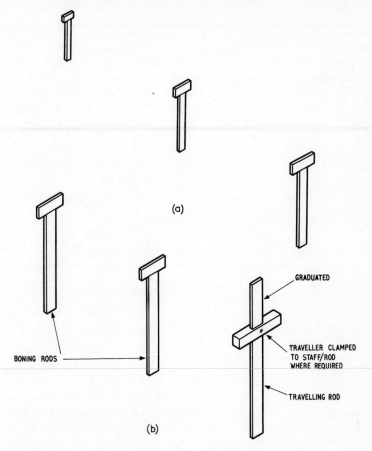

(a)

GRADUATED

BONING RODS ⎯⎯⎯⎯⎯⎯⎯⎯⎯⎯⎯⎯⎯⎯⎯⎯⎯⎯⎯⎯⎯⎯➤

TRAVELLER CLAMPED
TO STAFF/ROD
WHERE REQUIRED

TRAVELLING ROD

(b)

Fig. 2.3. (a) Boning rods; (b) boning rods with travelling rod

do not have to be considered, while the set of boning rods with a *travelling rod* included would be used for straightforward levelling or where changes are required in the level surface.

When first using a set of boning rods it is essential that each rod be checked for accuracy of length and, where a travelling rod is included, that three rods of equal length can be obtained from the set (Fig. 2.3).

2.4 WOODEN SQUARE

The wooden square is used mainly for the purpose of setting out angles but may also be used as an aid for levelling.

The square varies in size from about 18 in. to 4 ft and it would not normally be necessary to use the smaller square for levelling.

The arm of a square may be used as a straight-edge providing it is known that the two edges of the arm are parallel, a spirit-level

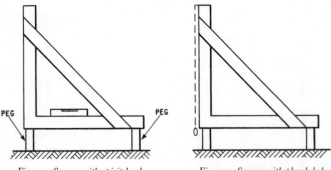

Fig. 2.4 Square with spirit-level   *Fig. 2.5. Square with plumb bob*

being used with the arm of the square to obtain the required levels (Fig. 2.4).

The wooden square may also be used together with a plumb bob secured to the vertical arm. The horizontal arm is placed on a known datum and the unknown height or level at the opposite end. The suspended plumb bob indicates by its relationship with the vertical arm when the unknown level corresponds with the known datum (Fig. 2.5).

2.5 THE A-LEVEL

The A-level consists of a wooden or steel frame shaped like the letter A, containing two legs and a horizontal arm. The legs may be fixed or have adjustable ends.

The level is used mainly for obtaining or determining levels over small obstructions by placing one leg on a known datum and the second leg on the unknown height so that the horizontal arm acts as a bridge.

The horizontal arm may contain a spirit-level inset centrally or

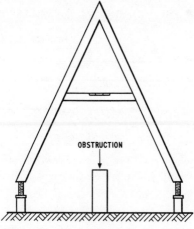

OBSTRUCTION

Fig. 2.6. A-level

a plumb bob suspended from the vertex at the head of the frame and terminating at the horizontal arm, which in this case would be graduated from the centre to each of the legs (Fig. 2.6).

2.6 USING THE SPIRIT-LEVEL

We know that the spirit-level contains a bubble-tube in which is contained a fluid. When the spirit-level is tilted a bubble in the tube will move along its length. It follows that when a spirit-level is known to be accurate a level plane will be produced when the bubble is in the centre of its run in the tube.

Normally a spirit-level would be used in conjunction with a straight-edge but the 3 ft long levels can be used by themselves for short distances (Fig. 2.7).

If A is a known datum, place a peg at B, place the spirit-level on A and B, lower or raise B accordingly until the bubble is in the centre of its run. A and B are now level.

When a vertical plane such as the quoin of a wall has to be checked for accuracy the 3 ft long spirit-level is the most suitable, while for gateposts or similar fixtures a pocket-sized spirit-level is suitable, providing it contains a circular level.

In this case the spirit-level is placed upon the vertical surface and when the bubble is in the centre of its run that surface is vertical.

To understand the movement of the bubble the reader must

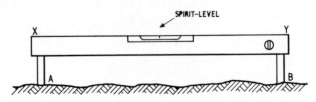

Fig. 2.7. *Straight-edge and spirit-level*

remember that when the bubble is on the left of centre the right-hand side is lower and when it is on the right of centre the left-hand side is lower.

2.7 USING THE STRAIGHT-EDGE

The straight-edge may be used to determine the difference in level between any two positions within or outside its own length, but in

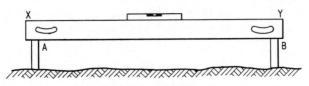

Fig. 2.8. *Producing level* B *from datum* A

each case requires the aid of a spirit-level for short distances and a spirit-level and boning rods for extended distances.

To place a peg B level to peg A a single length straight-edge may be used (Fig. 2.8).

Call the straight-edge X—Y, and peg A a datum, place the end of the straight-edge X on peg A with Y on peg B. Place a spirit-level at mid-distance on the straight-edge, raise or lower peg B until the bubble of the spirit-level is in the centre of its run; pegs A and B are then level with each other.

To extend a level from A to C which is more than one length of straight-edge distance.

With peg A as a datum and X—Y the straight-edge, place X on

the peg A and Y on the peg B. Using a spirit-level placed upon the straight-edge establish peg B level with peg A (Fig. 2.9).

Move the straight-edge so that Y remains on peg B and X is placed on peg C; use a spirit-level placed upon the straight-edge

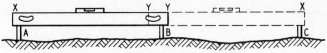

Fig. 2.9. Extending level at peg A to peg C

to establish peg C level with peg B. Peg C is now level with pegs A and B.

Although the term *levelling* is used this does not always mean that one peg must be *level* with another peg. The term *levelling* must be considered also in relation to a *rise* or a *fall* from one peg to another.

To establish a *fall* from peg A to peg B (Fig. 2.10) using straight-edge X—Y, with A as the datum, place X on peg A, place a 1 in. thick wooden block on top of peg B and place Y on this block. Place

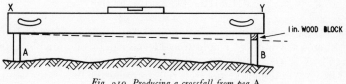

Fig. 2.10. Producing a crossfall from peg A

a spirit-level on the straight-edge and lower peg B until the bubble of the spirit-level is in the centre of its run.

Remove the spirit-level, straight-edge and wooden block. Peg B is now 1 in. lower than peg A and is said to have 1 in. of fall. If the distance A to B is 6 ft it is said that A to B = *crossfall* of 1 in 72 or if it is a longitudinal direction or for a drain it has a *gradient* of 1 in 72 (6 ft by 12 = 72 in. at 1 in.; difference in level = 1 in 72).

When using a straight-edge and spirit-level on a site a periodic check should be made to ensure the spirit-level is accurate.

Using a 6 ft long straight-edge place pegs A and B 5 ft apart. Mark the mid-distance on the straight-edge, measure each side of this mark to represent the exact length of the spirit-level (Fig. 2.11).

Consider peg A as the datum; place one end of the straight-edge on A and the other end on peg B. Place the spirit-level within the margin marked on the straight-edge and produce B level with A.

Leave the straight-edge in position, take the spirit-level off the straight-edge and reverse it, replace the spirit-level in the margin on the straight-edge.

If the spirit-level is accurate and the straight-edge has not been moved, the bubble will be in the centre of its run. If the bubble is

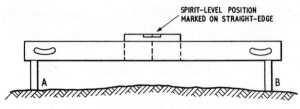

Fig. 2.11. Checking accuracy of a spirit-level

found to be off-centre, recheck as before; if it is still found to be off-centre the bubble-tube will require adjusting.

A good-quality spirit-level will contain adjustment screws which can be manipulated to rectify any errors.

2.8 USING BONING RODS

The principle of boning rods is that if any two positions or levels are known any number of additional levels can be obtained by using three boning rods each of equal length (Fig. 2.12).

The correct use of boning rods requires that the two outer boning rods be held on established levels, A and B. A sight is made over the top of the boning rod at A to the top of the boning rod at B. The intermediate level peg C is to be established and the third boning rod is held on the peg C.

When sighting from A to B the top of the boning rod C will be found above or below the line of sight (*line of collimation*), necessitating that the peg C be lowered or raised to establish a level where the tops of pegs A, C, B will be parallel to the line of collimation produced by the tops of the boning rods. This is sometimes referred to as a *straight bone* and means that a line produced over the tops of the three pegs will be parallel to a line produced over the tops of the boning rods (Fig. 2.12).

The term *back boning* is sometimes used to define a method used when pegs A and B are datums and peg C has to be produced as a continuation (Fig. 2.13).

In this case a boning rod is held at A and another at B, a third is

held at C which is the unknown level. A sight is made over the
boning rod at A, then over B, and the peg at C is raised or lowered

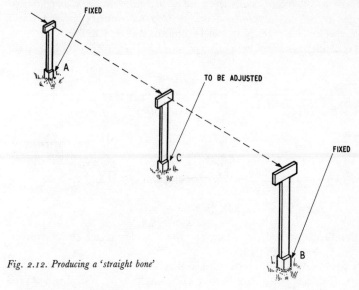

Fig. 2.12. Producing a 'straight bone'

until the top of the boning rod at C is in line with the tops of the
boning rods B and A.

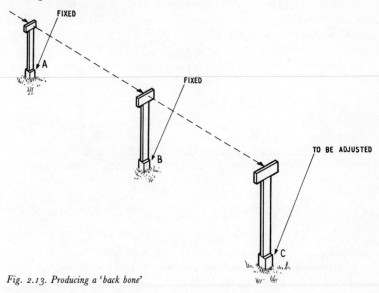

Fig. 2.13. Producing a 'back bone'

It is sometimes necessary to produce a number of pegs on a site that form a camber or a sag. This would be mainly used for the purpose of drainage, as in the case of a road, car park, precinct or similar paved area, where it is required to conduct surface water into courses from where it can be channelled into gullies.

To produce a camber section a set of boning rods which contain

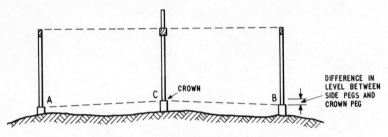

Fig. 2.14. Producing a crown level

a travelling rod will be required, the travelling rod being used to produce plus or minus levels.

If pegs A and B are datums and peg C is to be established to produce a camber section, a boning rod is held at A and another at B (Fig. 2.14).

The traveller on the travelling rod is fixed so that it is of less height than each of the boning rods and is held at C. A sight is made over the boning rod at A in the direction of the boning rod at B and the peg C is raised or lowered until the traveller corresponds with the

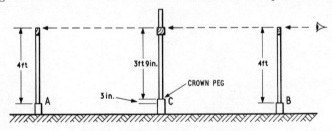

Fig. 2.15. Producing a level of 3 inches

sight line. A string line placed over the tops of pegs A, C, B will indicate the camber.

Example 1

Two pegs A and B have been established and peg C is to be fixed to provide a camber of 3 in. (Fig. 2.15).

Using two boning rods, each 4 ft long, and a travelling rod, position the traveller at 3 ft 9 in. Place a boning rod at A and another at B; place the travelling rod at C. Sight over the boning rod at A towards B; raise or lower peg C until the sight line is complete.

When a sag between two levels is required to form a valley curve, the middle peg will be the lower one. This type of section may be used when it is required to guide surface water into a central channel.

Example 2

Two pegs A and B have been established and peg C is to be fixed to provide a 3 in. sag (Fig. 2.16).

Using two boning rods, each 4 ft long, and a travelling rod,

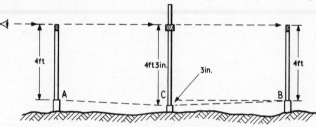

Fig. 2.16. Producing a sag of 3 inches

position the traveller at 4 ft 3 in. Place a boning rod at A and another at B; place the travelling rod at C. Sight over the boning rod at A towards B; raise or lower peg C until the sight line is complete.

Boning rods may also be used to determine existing levels and to

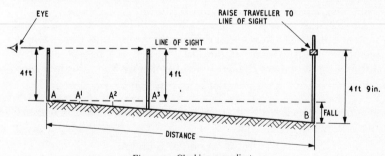

Fig. 2.17. Checking a gradient

produce gradients and for this a straight-edge, spirit-level and a set of boning rods would be used.

Assume it is required to know the amount of fall between A and B on a path with A as the datum (Fig. 2.17).

Place the straight-edge at A, use the straight-edge and spirit-level to produce pegs A^1, A^2 and A^3 in line with AB. Place a boning rod at A and another at A^3. Place a travelling rod at B with a loose traveller. Sight from the top of boning rod at A over the top of the boning rod at A^3 to the travelling rod at B. Signal for the traveller to be raised or lowered until the sight line is complete, secure the traveller and check the reading on the rod. If the two boning rods are each 4 ft long and the reading on the travelling rod is 4 ft 9 in., this indicates a fall of 9 in. from A to B.

Assume it is required to establish a gradient with a fall of 9 in. from A to B (Fig. 2.18). Place the straight-edge at the known datum A; produce pegs A^1, A^2 and A^3 in line with AB.

Place a peg at B. Set the traveller on the travelling rod at 4 ft 9 in.

Place the 4 ft long boning rods on datum A and peg A^3; sight from the top of the boning rod at A over the one at A^3 to the

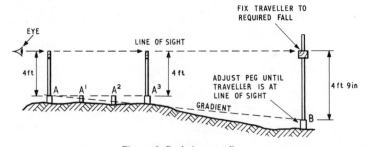

Fig. 2.18. Producing a gradient

travelling rod at B. Raise or lower peg at B until the line of sight is complete. The fall between A and B is 9 in.

In most cases a crossfall or a gradient will be expressed as a unit such as 1 in 48 or 1 in 100 and this simply means units rather than a particular measurement. If the distance between pegs A and B is 4 ft and the difference in level of the two pegs is 1 in., this indicates:

$$4 \times 12 = 48 \text{ in. at 1 in. fall} = 1 \text{ in } 48$$

If pegs A and B are 50 ft apart and the difference in level between the two pegs is 6 in., then:

$$50 \times 12 = 600 \text{ in. at 6 in. fall}$$
$$= 600 \div 6 = 1 \text{ in } 100$$

When determining or producing crossfall or gradient pegs on a site using boning rods, the distance between the two extreme pegs must be known so that the amount of fall can be calculated and vice versa.

2.9 CALCULATING CROSSFALLS AND GRADIENTS

A crossfall or a gradient will contain: (1) distance between two points; (2) fall between two points; (3) crossfall or gradient between two points. If any two are known the third can be calculated.

Examples

(1) A drain is 100 ft long and has 6 in. fall; calculate the gradient:

distance $\quad$ = 100 ft and fall = 6 in.

100×12 = 1,200 in.

$1,200 \div 6$ = 200 = 1 in 200 gradient

(2) A drain has a gradient of 1 in 200 and a fall of 6 in.; calculate the distance:

gradient = 1 in 200 and fall = 6 in.

$200 \times \frac{1}{2}$ = 100 = 100 ft distance

(3) A drain has a distance of 100 ft and the gradient is 1 in 200; find the fall:

distance = 100 ft and gradient = 1 in 200

$\frac{100}{200}$ ft = $\frac{1}{2}$ ft = 6 in. fall

Chapter 3

INSTRUMENTS FOR LEVELLING

Instruments that are used for producing levels on sites mainly consist of a base upon which a telescope is mounted together with one or more spirit-levels as aids in producing a horizontal plane.

An instrument would be placed upon a tripod as a means of stabilising it while in use.

The Cowley automatic level does not rely on a telescope, however; its accuracy is based on the transfer of light rays using a number of mirrors contained inside a box similar to a camera.

3.1 THE TRIPOD

The instruments based on the principle of the telescope are normally set up on tripods made from hardwood and containing fixed or telescopic legs.

The head of the tripod contains the metal mounting upon which the instrument is secured. Some tripods contain a circular spirit-level which assists the user to set up the tripod so that its head is horizontal.

The design of heads varies and is made to suit certain instruments —some instruments are screwed on to the head, others are screwed from underneath the head, while some tripods have a patent domed head.

At the bottom of the tripod legs will normally be found steel feet which enable them to secure the tripod in the ground.

The Cowley level has a metal tripod 38 in. high with a pin, fixed at the head, inserted into an aperture at the base of the instrument.

3.2 THE TELESCOPE

The dumpy level and similar instruments contain a telescope which is used for sighting from an eyepiece at the viewing end, through a diaphragm near the viewing end and an object glass at the forward end.

Telescopes vary considerably in length but this does not make any difference to their efficiency, although some instruments will have variations which in appearance make them different. The telescope which consists of eyepiece, diaphragm and object glass is used essentially for observing an image such as a levelling staff efficiently, so that errors are kept at an absolute minimum.

The eyepiece, which is the viewing end, is capable of being rotated clockwise and anti-clockwise so that it moves in a longitudinal direction. The adjustment is used mainly to suit the eyesight of different observers but it is also required for adjustment of parallax.

When viewing through the eyepiece, the image is transferred through the object glass lens in the line of the diaphragm and the ray is transferred to the eyepiece to produce an inverted image.

When a clear image cannot be seen a focusing screw on the side of the telescope is rotated. This moves a lens along the inside of the telescope by means of a ratchet until the image becomes clear; by rotating in the opposite direction the image can disappear.

3.3 THE DIAPHRAGM

The diaphragm is sometimes referred to as the graticule and consists of a metal ring situated near to the eyepiece and is secured within the telescope by screws (Fig. 3.1).

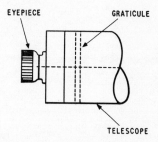

Fig. 3.1. Diaphragm or graticule

Some diaphragms have spiders' webs to indicate the lines when viewing from the eyepiece, but in general black lines etched on glass are found with most levelling instruments using this principle.

The formation of the lines varies with different instruments but the main horizontal and vertical lines are the important ones.

Another type of diaphragm consists of metal points for which special metal is used. While the web lines of the diaphragm enable

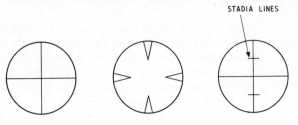

Fig. 3.2. *Types of diaphragm*

readings to be made on a levelling staff, with the metal points, the points themselves indicate the reading on a staff (Fig. 3.2).

3.4 STADIA LINES

In addition to the web lines on a diaphragm may be found two smaller horizontal lines, one above and one below the main horizontal web line. These are the stadia lines which are set at predetermined spacing normally to provide a multiplying constant of 1:100.

The stadia lines are used for tacheometry which is the measurement of distances, vertical and horizontal, at a given position from a station (Fig. 3.3). In the diagram, E is the eyepiece and A the staff.

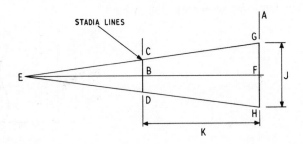

Fig. 3.3. *Stadia lines*

B is the horizontal web line with C and D the upper and lower stadia lines. F is the reading on the staff obtained by the web line; G and

H are the readings obtained by the stadia lines. J is the difference between G and H, with K the calculated distance.

3.5 THE BUBBLE-TUBE

While some variation in the design of levelling instruments will be found, accuracy in setting up all instruments for which the bubble-tube of the spirit-level is required should be understood (Fig. 3.4).

The spirit-level is fixed so that when levelling screws (sometimes

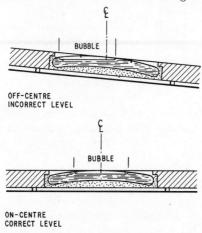

Fig. 3.4. Plain bubble-tube

referred to as foot screws) are manipulated the telescope will be horizontal when the bubble in the bubble-tube is in the centre of its run.

The glass tube is slightly curved and nearly filled with alcohol so that an air bubble remains in the tube.

The tube normally contains markings which indicate the highest part and further subdivisions on each side of the centre one.

When the spirit-level is not in the centre of its run it may only be partly visible. By manipulation of the levelling screws the bubble moves to the highest part of the tube until it is equally divided by the main line on the tube; it is then in the centre of its run.

Some instruments have the principle of a split bubble (Fig. 3.5). When observed, the bubble will be split in two parts; by manipulation of the appropriate part of the instruments (refer to makers' instructions) the two halves move together to produce one bubble.

The bubble in this case will be used for levelling up the telescope by manipulation of the elevating screw and normally used with 'precise' instruments.

Precise levelling on sites must always be carried out by using levelling instruments that are produced to enable exact levels to be

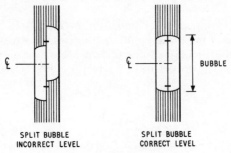

SPLIT BUBBLE   SPLIT BUBBLE
INCORRECT LEVEL   CORRECT LEVEL

Fig. 3.5. Split bubble

obtained, that is, taking into consideration the curvature of the earth's surface, and levelling is made on a site in relation to the earth's surface.

3.6 THE ABNEY LEVEL

The Abney level is a hand instrument used to determine the angle of inclination of the land; it is not used for establishing level pegs on a site.

The level consists of a sighting tube $4\frac{3}{4}$ in. long extending to 7 in. Near the object end of the tube is fixed a radius arc of $1\frac{1}{8}$ in. containing degrees and a vernier reading of 10 min.

To determine the degree of inclination the observer sights through the eyepiece, directing the object end of the tube on to

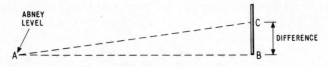

Fig. 3.6. Degree of inclination using the Abney level

a staff held by an assistant at the top of the incline and on to a mark on the staff equal to the height of the observer's eye above the ground where he is standing.

The bubble-tube and a movable pointer are rotated until the

bubble is seen to be central. The position of the pointer on the scale is inspected and the degree of inclination recorded.

Assume A is the observer's eye and C the mark on the staff; the degree of inclination is between AB and AC (Fig. 3.6).

3.7 THE WATER-LEVEL

A simple form of levelling instrument consists of a U-shaped glass tube containing water and fixed rigidly to a staff or stand (Fig. 3.7).

To use the water-level the instrument is set up vertically at a given height above ground level at A.

A measuring staff is held at B and a sight is made from the water-level X on to the staff at C to produce line of collimation XC.

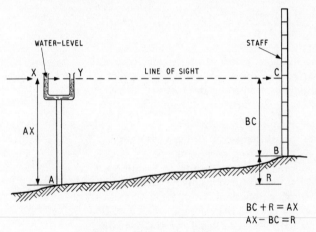

BC + R = AX
AX − BC = R

Fig. 3.7. Using a water-level

The measurement BC on the measuring staff is recorded and compared to the measurement AX, the difference being the vertical difference between AX and BC.

Assume the measurement AX is 4 ft and BC is 3 ft; the difference is 1 ft.

If the distance AB is 50 ft, with the difference in height AX, and BC is 1 ft, the gradient is expressed as 1 in 50.

The water-level indicates the principle of levelling; when the water in the tube at X—Y is horizontal the line or height of collimation will be the same and when the tube is tilted with Y higher than X, the line of collimation will be inclined.

3.8 THE WYE-LEVEL

The wye- or Y-levelling instrument has been superseded by 'precise' instruments, but students should know as much as possible about all methods and instruments available for levelling.

The wye-level contains a telescope and a spirit-level which rest on two Y-supports. The telescope is secured to the supports by means

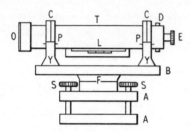

Fig. 3.8. The Wye-level

of two clamps. The Y-supports are secured to a bar which in turn is secured to a base. The whole instrument is fixed to a tripod for the purpose of levelling on a site (Fig. 3.8)

To know the instrument in detail:

E = eyepiece for sighting
D = diaphragm containing web lines
C = clamps to secure telescope
P = pins to secure clamps to Y-supports
Y = supports for holding the telescope
T = telescope
O = object end of telescope
L = spirit-level to 'level up' the instrument
B = bar carrying the Y-supports
F = base which is capable of rotating
A = parallel plates, the lower one being screwed on to a tripod
S = levelling screws which enable the telescope to be made horizontal or be tilted

3.9 THE DUMPY LEVEL

The levelling instrument referred to as a dumpy level may vary considerably by certain aids and refinements introduced by instrument makers; the basic details, however, are similar (Fig. 3.9).

The instrument would appear similar to the wye-level and to

some extent this is true. It will be seen, however, that the instrument does not contain Y-supports or clamps and the spirit-level will generally be found mounted on top or at the side of the telescope.

The instrument is fixed to a base with an upper parallel plate

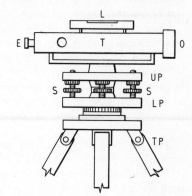

Fig. 3.9. The dumpy level

UP and a lower parallel plate *LP* separated by three or sometimes four levelling screws *S*, sometimes referred to as foot screws, which are used as the means for setting the instrument horizontal when fixed to a tripod *TP*.

When the instrument is set up on a tripod the line of collimation must be at right-angles to the vertical axis.

It will be seen that the instrument is set rigidly on its base but it can be rotated on a horizontal plane. When the instrument has been set up accurately the line of collimation will be the same throughout the horizontal plane.

Some dumpy levels will be found to have a hinged mirror set over the spirit-level which enables the movement of the bubble in the bubble-tube to be seen by diverting the eye from the eyepiece *E* on the telescope to the mirror to see the reflection of the bubble.

3.10 THE PRECISION LEVEL

The levelling instrument often referred to as a *quick-set* level is a precision instrument which may be claimed as an improvement compared to the dumpy level. Basically, the precision instrument is the same as the dumpy level, but instead of the telescope being fixed at right-angles to the vertical axis it is provided with a micrometer screw which may or may not be calibrated.

Manipulation of the micrometer screw enables the telescope to be tilted to plus or minus the horizontal plane.

Two spirit-levels are provided on the instrument, the normal long spirit-level mounted on the telescope and a smaller circular one, sometimes referred to as the *cat's-eye*, which is the aid for establishing the horizontal plane.

The precision instrument may contain parallel plates with levelling screws or it may have a quick-setting ball joint at its base.

It must be remembered that when this instrument is being used the bubble in the long spirit-level may be seen to 'move off centre', because on rotating the telescope the line of collimation is not fixed although the base of the instrument is fixed. This means that prior to taking readings through the telescope the long bubble must be checked for accuracy.

The precision levelling instrument fitted with a ball joint only is generally quicker to set up than one fitted with three or four levelling screws but this does not mean that the instrument is superior when used for levelling.

The instrument may sometimes contain a horizontal circle with a vernier scale fixed below the telescope. This enables horizontal angles on the site to be set out to an accuracy of five minutes of a degree.

It may also contain a gradienter screw positioned under the eye-piece end of the telescope, suitably graduated into divisions plus or

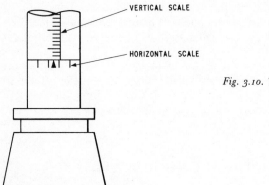

VERTICAL SCALE

HORIZONTAL SCALE

Fig. 3.10. The gradienter screw

minus, the horizontal plane allowing for one complete rotation of the screw for a gradient of 1 in 100. The subdivisions on the screw enable most designed gradients to be produced (Fig. 3.10).

Some instruments have gradienter screws, where one revolution of the screw = 1 in 1,000, plus or minus.

When using a precision instrument the instructions that are provided by the maker must be studied until all parts of the particular instrument are understood.

3.11 THE AUTOSET LEVEL

Unlike conventional levelling instruments, in which the line of collimation is always parallel to the axis of the telescope, the autoset level has an optical compensator which maintains a level line of collimation even though the instrument may be tilted as much as 15 minutes of arc (Fig. 3.11).

Fig. 3.11(a) shows that with a conventional level the line of sight

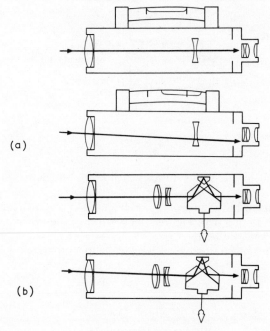

(a)

(b)

Fig. 3.11. Principle of the stabiliser

is level when the bubble is central. If the telescope is tilted then points on a level line are seen above or below the cross-line.

However, in the autoset level there is a stabiliser consisting of two prisms on a suspended mount. If the autoset is tilted the stabiliser hangs like a plumb bob and keeps the horizontal ray on the cross-lines automatically [Fig. 3.11(b)].

The compensator consists of a fixed roof prism above two swinging prisms supported on four metallic tapes forming a cross-spring flexure pivot. The ingenuity of design ensures a frictionless suspension having a repetition of setting better than 1 second of arc.

The fixed prism provides an erect image; the suspended prisms form a double-reflector which swings like a plumb bob and changes its angular relationship to the optical axis as the telescope is tilted.

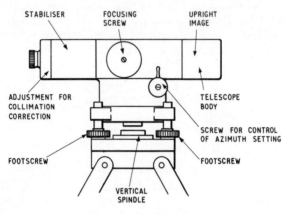

Fig. 3.12. The autoset level

The graticule may have metallised web lines and 1 : 100 stadia lines (Fig. 3.12).

The instrument has a horizontal circle graduated at 1 degree intervals from 0 to 360 deg. Figured every 10 deg, the circle is read through a magnifying lens.

In appearance the autoset level is more compact than many other levelling instruments.

Chapter 4

LEVELLING STAFFS

4.1 THE SOPWITH STAFF

The levelling staff most frequently used in Great Britain is the Sopwith staff which is graduated on the metric system and divided into feet. It is usually 14 ft long and may be of hinged or telescopic construction. The lower part of the telescopic staff is 5 ft long and into this slides the following $4\frac{1}{2}$ ft, followed again by the uppermost $4\frac{1}{2}$ ft.

When fully opened to its 14 ft length each section is held on to the lower section by means of a spring clip which when correctly positioned produces continuity for the full length of the staff.

The hinged or folding staff will be of solid construction but the telescopic type is made from mahogany protected by brass mountings and a brass shoe.

The face of the staff consists of black markings, black numerals and red numerals on a white ground. The lines or divisions are scaled in feet, tenths of feet and hundredths of feet (Fig. 4.1).

The readings on the Sopwith staff should be carefully studied so that a full understanding can be obtained.

The large *red* numerals indicate *feet*. The small red numerals indicate the section of staff when viewed through a levelling instrument and a large red numeral is not visible, as may be found when sighting over a short distance.

The *black* numerals indicate *inches* as decimals.

To avoid possible errors when reading numbers on the staff through a levelling instrument, the figure 5 is replaced by the Roman numeral V. The figure 9 may be replaced by the letter N or the top loop of the 9 may be blocked in. The figure 10 will invariably be replaced by the Roman numeral X.

33

The red numerals are on the left-hand side of the Sopwith staff and should be studied on an actual staff to fully understand them and to see where they commence and where they terminate.

It will be seen that all large *red* numerals are placed with the top of the numeral corresponding with the top of a long black line,

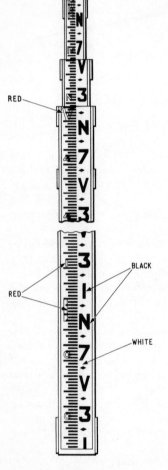

Fig. 4.1. The Sopwith levelling staff

although at first glance they may appear to terminate at the black line.

On the right-hand side of the Sopwith staff are black numerals all indicating *odd* values, commencing with the numeral 1 and terminating with 9 or N, and each is repeated throughout each foot of the staff. It will also be seen that the top of each black numeral corresponds with the top of a long black line and this indicates the reading.

Even numerals, 2, 4, 6, 8 and 10, are not shown as black numerals but the measurements or readings are indicated by the long black lines at the bottom of each black numeral. It must be appreciated that if all divisions represented by the long black lines were marked by numerals the numerals would merge into each other and this could produce inaccuracies when reading the staff.

Between the black numerals will be seen a black diamond or a small circle with a line passing through it; this indicates the reading of 0·05 in each of the divisions.

To understand the Sopwith staff fully, commence at the bottom

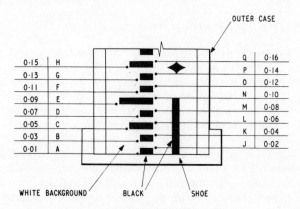

Fig. 4.2. Understanding the Sopwith levelling staff

where a brass shoe will be found; this has a value of 0·01 ft and is equal in thickness to each black line or white division.

Immediately above the shoe will be seen a small black line, the top of which indicates an *even* reading. Above this is the white background which provides a white line between two black lines; the top of this is an *odd* reading. Continuing up the staff we now find that the top of each *white* is an *odd* reading and the top of each *black* is an *even* reading.

We now find that the *odd* readings, indicated by letters A to H inclusive, are (Fig. 4.2):

$$
\begin{array}{ll}
A = 0\cdot01 & E = 0\cdot09 \\
B = 0\cdot03 & F = 0\cdot11 \\
C = 0\cdot05 & G = 0\cdot13 \\
D = 0\cdot07 & H = 0\cdot15
\end{array}
$$

and the *even* readings indicated by the letters J to Q inclusive are:

$$
\begin{array}{ll}
J = 0\cdot02 & N = 0\cdot10 \\
K = 0\cdot04 & O = 0\cdot12 \\
L = 0\cdot06 & P = 0\cdot14 \\
M = 0\cdot08 & Q = 0\cdot16
\end{array}
$$

The letter N indicates that this is tenths of a foot and is, therefore, the first inch and recorded as 0·10. It will also be seen that the top of the numeral 1 also corresponds to this. It will also be seen that the black diamond corresponds with the reading 0·15, indicating the value of 0·05, but is not found in the lower reading of 0·05 because of the numeral 1, remembering that the diamond or circle will be found between the black numerals.

4.1.1 READING THE SOPWITH STAFF

When observing the Sopwith staff through the telescope of a levelling instrument it will be seen that the numerals are upside down because of the complex system used in the instrument. This, however, is not unusual when it is considered that when looking into a mirror the image is reversed; if we look into a mirror and touch the left ear, the image in the mirror shows the right ear apparently being touched.

Because from an early age people are accustomed to mirrors, they regard mirror-images as normal, but are liable to be confused when observing a Sopwith staff upside down. However, after a short practical period of observing the staff through the telescope of a levelling instrument it will be found that it is possible to master all readings.

While it is possible to obtain staffs with numerals upside down so that they appear correct when observed through the telescope, equal confusion can be found when trying to understand the reading on a staff without using the instrument.

It is advisable to master the readings on the staff before attempting practical readings with an instrument, so that the correct value of each division represented by the black and white marks can be understood. Once the readings in a complete foot margin have been mastered, the remainder is repetition apart from the addition of the feet readings represented by the *red* numerals.

When learning to read the staff without a levelling instrument (Fig. 4.3):

$$
\begin{array}{ll}
A = 1\cdot01 & F = 1\cdot02 \\
B = 1\cdot03 & G = 1\cdot04
\end{array}
$$

C = 1·05   H = 1·06   L = 1·70
D = 1·07   J = 1·08   and: M = 2·00
E = 1·09   K = 1·10   N = 2·05

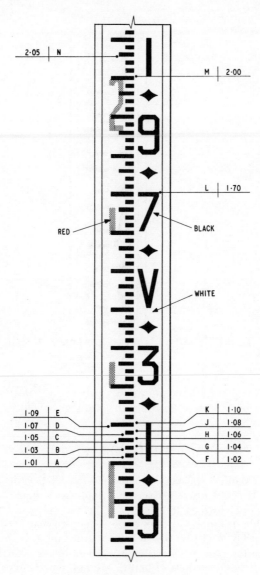

Fig. 4.3. Reading the levelling staff without using a levelling instrument

The same readings are now observed with the staff upside down (Fig. 4.4).

While it may appear confusing commence at A = 1·01, remem-

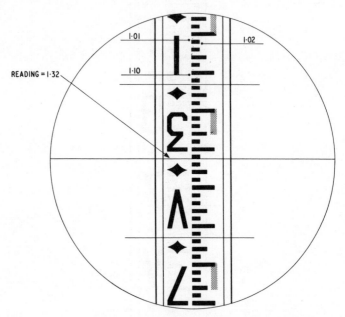

Fig. 4.4. Reading the Sopwith levelling staff through the telescope

bering that *top of white = odd reading*, progress to *top of the black* to find F = 1·02 = *even reading* until the readings have been mastered.

4.2 THE GAYER STAFF

The Gayer staff is a specially designed staff which permits easy direct readings. It comprises a silk screen printed scale figured in tenths, and graduated to 0·02 ft, which can be very clearly seen from a considerable distance. All ambiguity of figuring has been removed. The actual figure cut by the web line is the one to be booked, and the graduation bars, each representing 0·02 ft, are clear figures.

The horizontal sections of figures are also 0·02 ft high, and both bars and white spaces are simply bisected to read 0·01 ft (Fig. 4.5).

4.3 THE INVAR STAFF

The Invar staff is an engine-divided Invar strip with two scales divided either in British or metric measurements, mounted on an

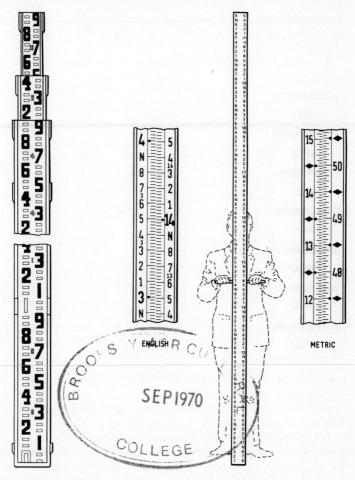

Fig. 4.5. The Gayer staff   Fig. 4.6. The Invar staff

extended aluminium alloy body under spring tension. The staff is available singly or in pairs. Each staff has a circular bubble, folding handles and steadying rods.

British scale is graduated to 0·02 ft; thickness of engraved line is

0·04 in. Metric scale is graduated to 5 mm; thickness of line is 1 mm (Fig. 4.6).

4.4 THE SCOTCH STAFF

The Scotch staff is 14 ft long, divided into three sections, and is 2 in. by 1 in. in section. When in use the sections are socketed together (Fig. 4.7).

The staff has a white background with black lines superimposed

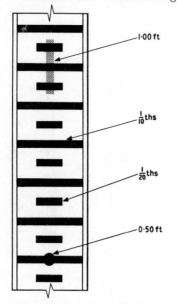

Fig. 4.7. The Scotch staff

upon it to provide divisions of one-tenth of a foot with shorter black lines to indicate twentieths.

Feet are indicated by large *red* numerals, and black circles indicate half-feet.

It may be claimed that because the Scotch staff contains fewer numerals it is easier to understand, while on the other hand it must be understood that some estimation of readings has to be made because hundredths of feet are not provided as in the case of the Sopwith staff.

4.5 THE PLAIN STAFF

The Plain staff is suitable where a series of levels or heights all on the same horizontal plane are to be produced. The staff consists of a wooden rod 8 ft long and about 2 in. by 1 in. in section and does not contain any divisions.

Fixed to the rod is a target bar painted white with a black line painted across it, or a circular disc divided into one black semi-circle and one white semi-circle with the dividing line horizontal, or it may be divided into four quadrants which will provide a horizontal and a vertical line.

This staff requires little technical knowledge when being used, because the height of collimation is produced and fixed by securing the target bar or disc at position A and when moved to position B the same observation is made through the telescope of the levelling instrument and the height at B raised or lowered until the height of collimation is the same as that at position A.

4.6 CARE OF A LEVELLING STAFF

A levelling staff will last for many years if care is taken on the site and when storing it in an office.

While levelling instruments would not normally be used during heavy rain, it is very likely that a levelling staff will become wet from time to time and at such times it should be wiped dry with a soft cloth before being placed in store.

The face of a staff containing readings should not become scratched. If pencil marks are used to indicate a reading, they should be cleaned off the face the same day.

When used in water for marine purposes the staff must be wiped clean and dry each time it is taken out of the water and not only before being placed in store.

When placed in store a staff should be placed upright at floor level or if placed horizontally it should be above floor level on a shelf.

When moving about on a site the staff should be carried with the topmost section forward so that it is visible at all times.

When opening a telescopic staff, care must be taken to see that the spring clip which engages each section is in its correct position and secure.

An assistant holding a staff while readings are being made upon it should stand behind the staff with a hand placed at each side of it so that it is held vertical and hands are clear of the readings.

Wherever possible the sun should be directed towards a staff when readings are being taken, so that when setting up a levelling instrument the sun should be at the rear or side of the person who will be taking readings through the telescope.

Chapter 5

USING LEVELLING
INSTRUMENTS

5.1 HAND SIGNALS

On most construction sites one can expect a considerable amount of noise, such as that caused by the movement of mechanical plant and transport, and in most cases an assistant holding a levelling staff will be some distance from the person using the levelling instrument.

It will, therefore, be realised that for communication to be made and understood between the two persons, something other than vocal sounds is necessary in order that the assistant will know what the observer requires without having to move unnecessarily about the site.

The following is a series of hand and arm signals which provide a suitable means of communication, providing both persons understand them and they are adhered to (Fig. 5.1):

Fig. 5.1	*Message*	*Signal*
(a)	*move to my left*	move left arm over 90°
(b)	*move to my right*	move right arm over 90°
(c)	*move top of staff to my left*	move left arm over 30°
(d)	*move top of staff to my right*	move right arm over 30°
(e)	*raise height peg or staff*	extend arm horizontally and move hand upwards
(f)	*lower height peg or staff*	extend arm horizontally and move hand downwards

Fig. 5.1	*Message*	*Signal*
(g)	*establish the position*	extend both arms outwards slightly and thrust downwards
(h)	*return to me*	extend arm and place hand on top of head

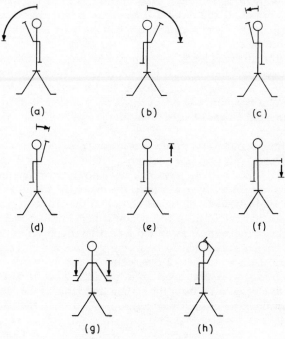

Fig. 5.1. Hand signals to use on a site

Other hand signals which are suitable as a means of communication can be adopted and can be appreciated if an assistant holding a levelling staff is trying to understand what an observer using the instrument requires.

5.2 SETTING UP A TRIPOD

Before going on to a site make certain that all equipment is in good condition, even to the extent of removing the levelling instrument from its case and checking the various parts.

Make certain that the correct position of the instrument when in its case is known, so that it will not be found difficult to replace on completion of levelling.

The levelling instrument is set up on a tripod which may contain fixed rigid or collapsible legs. Choose a station on a site that is free from mechanical plant, transport and obstructions. Set up the tripod with one of its legs on the left- and another on the right-hand side. Use the footplate at the lower ends of the legs to fix the legs firmly into the ground. If the ground is hard, as in the case of a paved surface, place an object such as a brick at each leg to prevent them slipping on the surface.

If the instrument is being used upon a highway suitable warning for approaching vehicles must be provided. If the instrument is set up in a field where cattle are grazing, and if suitable protection in the form of a temporary barrier cannot be provided, it must not be left unattended otherwise cattle may use it as a scratching pole and cause damage.

Set up the tripod so that the top is about chest level or just below shoulder level; this provides a suitable height when the instrument is set on the tripod without having to stoop down or stretch upwards.

Remove the protective cover from the top of the tripod and place it on the screw head to be found on one of the tripod legs. Adjust the legs so that the head of the tripod is horizontal. Some tripods contain a circular bubble as an aid for setting them up.

If the chosen station has to be where vehicles are moving about on a site, place a number of obstructions such as wooden stakes, pipes or bricks a few feet away from the legs. This helps to guide drivers of vehicles away from the station and reduces the vibrations created in the ground that may continuously disturb the tripod.

5.3 SETTING UP A THREE-SCREW LEVELLING INSTRUMENT

Open the case containing the instrument and note exactly how it is positioned, so that when returning it little difficulty will be found. It should be known that an instrument will be positioned in a certain way to restrict its movement when being carried in the case.

Detach any fastenings between the case and the instrument and remove the instrument, using one hand, making certain a firm grip has been obtained. Use the second hand to close the cover of the case and place the case between the legs of the tripod. As the case will normally contain small items such as a plumb bob, spanners and possibly a small screwdriver, it should at all times be kept with the cover uppermost.

Grip the top of the telescope firmly in one hand and lower the base of the instrument on to the head of the tripod.

If the method of securing to the tripod is by an extended thread on the head of the tripod, move the base of the instrument slightly

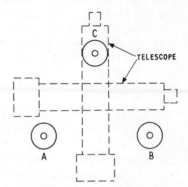

Fig. 5.2. Levelling a three-screw instrument

anti-clockwise until the threads are found to engage and then rotate slowly in a clockwise direction so that the base will screw on to the head.

Fouling the base of the instrument or the head of the tripod by cross-threading can result if care is not taken to ensure that threads are engaged at the commencement.

When the instrument is secured by a screw head pushed up through the head of the tripod, place the instrument accurately on to the tripod with one hand, use the other hand to pass the screw head through the aperture and gently turn anti-clockwise until it is found to engage and then clockwise to secure the instrument. The final turn on the screw in each case should be to 'thumb tight' and not 'wrist tight'. The screw head on a tripod is of a suitable length to ensure security without over-tightening.

Rotate the telescope until it is parallel with the screws *A* and *B* (Fig. 5.2).

Place a forefinger and thumb on screws *A* and *B*, take a reasonable grip on each screw and rotate slowly screw *B* anti-clockwise and screw *A* clockwise. Manipulate these screws and watch the bubble in the spirit level fixed to the instrument. The bubble will almost follow the movement of the left hand as it starts to move along the tube. Rotation of the screws in any direction should cease once the bubble is in the centre of its run.

When manipulating the screws both of them should be rotated simultaneously. Do not move one screw alone, even slightly, otherwise undue stress will be placed upon it.

The telescope is now rotated until it is at 90° to the first position; this will mean that one end of the telescope will be over screw C. The instrument is again levelled up until the bubble is in the centre of its run. The telescope is returned to the original position at AB and this time less adjustment of the screws is required. It is then rotated to screw C and levelled up again.

The telescope is rotated over a full 360° to make certain the bubble remains in the centre of its run; if it does not, a final adjustment will be required.

5.4 SETTING UP A FOUR-SCREW LEVELLING INSTRUMENT

The base of the four-screw levelling instrument is secured to the tripod in the same way as that for the three-screw method.

The telescope is placed over one pair of screws A–A (Fig. 5.3).

The screws A–A are rotated using the forefingers and thumbs until the bubble in the spirit-level is in the centre of its run. The telescope is rotated to 90° until it is positioned over the screws B–B

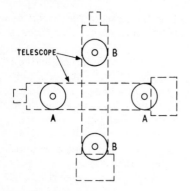

Fig. 5.3. Levelling a four-screw instrument

and the instrument levelled up again until the bubble is in the centre of its run. Return the telescope to the previous position at A–A and manipulate these screws if the bubble has moved. Return the telescope to B–B and repeat again if necessary until the bubble remains in the centre of its run all the time when the instrument has been set up.

Precision instruments normally contain two spirit-levels, a small circular level to enable the base of the instrument to be levelled up and an elongated spirit-level for use with the telescope.

When levelling up the base the small round bubble must be central to the etched circle provided on the level glass and in this case the elongated spirit-level at the side or on top of the telescope is not brought into use at this stage.

5.5 SETTING UP A QUICK-SET LEVELLING INSTRUMENT

The quick-set level contains a ball-and-socket joint for the base and it is generally considered that to set up this instrument less time is required.

The instrument must be treated in the same way as a three- or four-screw instrument, when mounting it on a tripod, to prevent fouling the screw threads.

The base contains a finger-grip ring that enables it to be secured 'thumb tight'. Above this is a knurled-edge ring bounding the ball-and-socket joint. The instrument is manipulated while the ring is loose until the small round bubble is within the etched circle. The ring is then slowly tightened and the telescope rotated over 90°. The position of the bubble is checked, and if it has moved outside the circle the ring is moved anti-clockwise a small amount and the instrument again manipulated until the bubble is accurate.

The instrument will have been set up when the bubble remains inside the circle when the telescope is positioned at each 90° of its complete rotation.

Final adjustment before readings can be made through the instrument have to be made, and this involves checking the elongated spirit-level to level up the telescope.

5.6 FOCUSING

Before a levelling instrument can be used for reading the levelling staff or for seeing ranging poles, the lenses must be set the correct distance apart to obtain a clear vision.

The telescope is lined on to the object, such as a levelling staff or ranging pole, by sighting over the top or along the side of the telescope so that the eyepiece at the viewing end and the cover at the object-glass end of the telescope are in line with the object. This preliminary lining up will bring the object within vision.

The screw which secures the telescope to the base is tightened.

The flap of the cover at the object-glass end is opened and made to hang downwards.

On most instruments the elongated bubble is positioned on the left-hand side of the telescope and if the left eye can be used as the 'viewing eye', this enables a constant check to be made on the elongated bubble through the angled mirror.

The eye is placed at the eyepiece which is manipulated until the cross-lines on the diaphragm are clear. The focusing screw is then manipulated until the object is clearly seen. If the object is not central to the line of sight, manipulation of the traversing screw will move the telescope to the left or the right to bring the object into view.

The focusing obtained by one observer may not be suitable for another, but only the slightest adjustment should be required to alter focus.

5.7 PARALLAX

When looking through the eyepiece any apparent movement between the cross-lines, relative to the levelling staff, is known as parallax and if not corrected can produce errors in readings.

When looking through the telescope, move the eye up and down a small amount and see if the movement is apparent.

To cure parallax, manipulate the eyepiece until a sharp view of the diaphragm lines is seen. Re-focus the telescope until a clear vision of the levelling staff is obtained.

Repeat the test previously mentioned for parallax; if still apparent repeat the cure.

If care is taken in the initial focusing of the telescope, parallax will not be produced.

5.8 SETTING ALIGNMENT PEGS

When level pegs are to be established on a site a large number of them will correspond with pegs indicating the building line, edge of carriageway or a particular line controlling construction, and these would normally be set out in advance of levelling to produce height or level pegs.

A levelling instrument may be used for producing the alignment of pegs and if the instrument has a horizontal scale above the parallel plates or ball-and-socket joint of the base, several lines at an angle to the main baseline can be set out as in the case of a building.

A datum peg indicating a tangent or a particular part of the main line will have been provided on the site or can be established after consulting the site plan.

The tripod is set up over the peg and the instrument secured as previously mentioned. On the underside of the instrument will be found a small hook which is visible through the aperture at the head of the tripod when viewed from the underside.

The plumb bob found in the instrument case is extended and the cord placed on the hook so that the plumb bob is suspended directly over the part of the peg indicating the actual line. This may be in the form of a nail or an etched line in the top of the peg.

If this part of the work is carried out on a windy day, it is advisable to provide some protection during the setting up to prevent movement of the plumb bob suspended over the peg. This can often be done by an assistant standing on the windward side with a coat opened fully so that the wind by-passes the instrument. The instrument is set up with the telescope directed towards the first peg to be produced.

Measure the required distance from the datum peg, say 50 ft, and mark an arc on the ground. An assistant now holds a ranging pole on this arc at the approximate position for the peg.

The telescope is now set and focused so that the web lines and vision are clear. Hand signals are given to guide the ranging pole on to the line of sight. When the ranging pole is cut by the vertical web line of the diaphragm seen through the telescope, manipulate the micrometer or gradienter screw below the eyepiece so that the web line moves down the ranging pole to the ground where it is to be inserted. The bottom of the ranging pole must coincide with the vertical web line at ground level.

The diaphragm of some instruments will be found to contain the main vertical web line and two smaller ones parallel with it, so that when sighting on to a ranging pole the two lines are guides for the two sides of the ranging pole and an estimate does not have to be made when deciding whether the vertical web line is central or not.

When the position has been established a peg is driven into the ground. The ranging pole is placed on top of the peg and this is again 'sighted in'. On establishing the correct position on the peg a mark is made on top of the peg by means of a nail or an etched line.

If the ground is too hard to drive a peg into, the surface may be marked, by chalk or charcoal or by etching, with a small encircled cross with the centre of the cross as the correct position.

5.9 PRODUCING ANGLES

When an instrument is not available for setting out angles from a baseline on a site, the 3:4:5 principle may be used but should be confined in measurements.

The principle is a well-known one where the sum of the square of 3 and of 4 equals the square of 5.

This may be shown as $3^2+4^2 = 5^2$

$$3 \times 3 = 9$$
$$4 \times 4 = 16$$
$$\text{sum} = 25$$
$$\text{and } 5 \times 5 = 25$$

It follows that any unit may be used providing it is maintained throughout. For site works the following are suitable:

$$3 \text{ ft}, \quad 4 \text{ ft and} \quad 5 \text{ ft} = 3{:}4{:}5 \times 1 = 33 \text{ ft tape}$$
$$6 \text{ ft}, \quad 8 \text{ ft and} \ 10 \text{ ft} = 3{:}4{:}5 \times 2 = 33 \text{ ft tape}$$
$$9 \text{ ft}, \ 12 \text{ ft and} \ 15 \text{ ft} = 3{:}4{:}5 \times 3 = 66 \text{ ft tape}$$
$$12 \text{ ft}, \ 16 \text{ ft and} \ 20 \text{ ft} = 3{:}4{:}5 \times 4 = 66 \text{ ft tape}$$
$$15 \text{ ft}, \ 20 \text{ ft and} \ 25 \text{ ft} = 3{:}4{:}5 \times 5 = 66 \text{ ft tape}$$

up to a multiplication of 10 which produces 30 ft, 40 ft and 50 ft

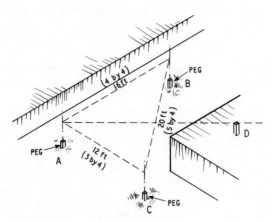

Fig. 5.4. Producing a right-angle with measuring tape

beyond which some error can be expected because of the sag in the tape or because of high winds.

To set out the angle on a baseline using one tape 66 ft long and
× 4 (Fig. 5.4).

A–B is the baseline, with A the datum peg. Measure A to C 12 ft,
measure C to B another 20 ft, making a total of 32 ft on the tape.
Extend the tape a further 16 ft to make a total of 48 ft on the tape.

At A, hold the end of the tape and the 48 ft marking; at C, hold
the 12 ft marking; at B, hold the 32 ft marking. Using two assistants
hold the tape taut at A, C and B; place a peg at C. The peg C is
marked and the line AC is at 90° to AB.

The quick-set and similar instruments contain a horizontal circular scale normally graduated so that almost any horizontal angle
can be set out.

When the instrument is set up the scale is placed with 0 and 180°
on the main line AB with zero at A. The telescope is lined on to B
from A and then rotated clockwise 90° so the telescope is lined to C.
The telescope is clamped and focused and a peg sighted in at C to
produce the right-angle ABC.

To set out the line AD which bisects the angle ABC rotate the
telescope anti-clockwise until the reading on the scale is −45°,
clamp the telescope, focus and sight in a peg at D.

As the horizontal circular scale is a full circle it contains 360°
and each degree contains 60′. If the scale was set with 0 and 180°
as the main line with zero at A, the reading for D would be 225° and
for C 270°.

While the instrument is set up at A it can be used for establishing
level pegs on any of the lines set out.

Chapter 6

RECORDING AND CALCULATING READINGS

6.1 USE OF INSTRUMENT AND STAFF

To find the difference in level between two points on the land of a suitable distance apart to permit the use of a levelling instrument and staff, a suitable station is chosen between the two points A and B so that the instrument can be set up.

The station S need not be on the line AB but should be free from

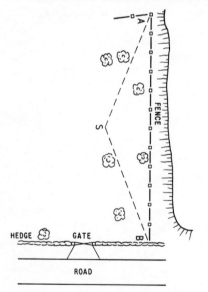

Fig. 6.1. Sight lines from a station

obstructions so that a sight line SA and SB can be obtained (Fig. 6.1). The instrument is set up at S with the levelling staff held at A and a reading is taken. The staff is then held at B, the instrument is checked and a reading is taken.

The difference between the reading A and the reading B is the difference in level between the two points.

The reading recorded in each case is that which coincides with the main horizontal web line produced when the eyepiece is manipulated on the telescope and after parallax has been eliminated.

It should be understood that the greater the staff reading the *lower* the point and the smaller the staff reading the *higher* the point.

It will be seen that when points A and B are to be checked and *S* is the station where the instrument is set up, a fuller understanding

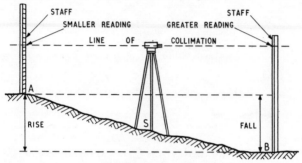

Fig. 6.2. Line of collimation from instrument to staff

is obtained in levelling procedure (Fig. 6.2).

The difference in the readings obtained at A and B indicate a *rise* from B to A or a *fall* from A to B.

If A is the first reading to be taken and B the second, the result will be a *fall*, while if B is first and A second, the result will be a *rise*.

Assume when taking readings A = 4·50 and B = 6·24, the result will be A to B = *fall* of 1·74 and vice versa.

It will also be seen that the line of sight from the levelling instrument to the staff in each case produces what is sometimes referred to as the *height of instrument* but is more correctly called the *line of collimation* or *height of collimation*.

6.2 LEVEL BOOKS

When recording readings that are taken two methods are available —the *rise-and-fall method* and the *height of collimation method*—both of which produce the same answer although the method of recording and calculation is different.

Level books for each method can be purchased but a student

should first learn to make his own so that the respective columns can be memorised.

A level book is normally about 6 in. by 4 in. in size, so that it is easy to handle and can be placed in the average coat pocket.

The headings used for the respective columns (shown below) may vary slightly but it will be seen that the essential headings which refer to the readings will be in the same order.

HEADINGS FOR RISE-AND-FALL METHOD

(1) *Position*   *Distance*   *Back Sight*   *Intermediate Sight*   *Fore Sight*   *Rise*   *Fall*   *Reduced Level*   *Remarks*

(2) *Remarks*   *Distance*   *Total Distance*   *Position*   *Back Sight*   *Intermediate Sight*   *Fore Sight*   *Rise*   *Fall*   *Reduced Level*

HEADINGS FOR HEIGHT OF COLLIMATION METHOD

(1) *Position*   *Distance*   *Back Sight*   *Intermediate Sight*   *Fore Sight*   *Height of Collimation*   *Reduced Level*   *Remarks*

(2) *Remarks*   *Distance*   *Total Distance*   *Position*   *Back Sight*   *Intermediate Sight*   *Fore Sight*   *Height of Collimation*   *Reduced Level*

For the rise-and-fall method the essential headings are: Distance, Back Sight, Intermediate Sight, Fore Sight, Rise, Fall and Reduced Level, and for the height of collimation method the essential headings are: Distance, Back Sight, Intermediate Sight, Fore Sight, Height of Collimation and Reduced Level.

The Remarks column is to enable certain features to be recorded, such as manholes, steps, etc., where readings have been taken, so that reference may be made to that feature later.

6.3 SIGHTS

It has been seen that the sights obtained when viewing through a levelling instrument are divided into *back sight, intermediate sight* and *fore sight,* and it must be understood that when an instrument is set up at a station the readings taken from that station are:

back sight   = the *first* reading
intermediate sight = all other readings except the last reading
fore sight   = the *last* reading (Fig. 6.3)

The same method of recording the readings is used for both types of level book.

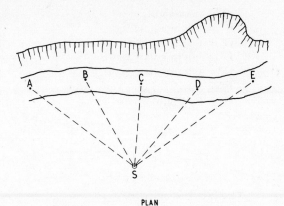

PLAN

Fig. 6.3. Names of sights (A, *back sight;* B, C, D, *intermediate
sights;* E, *fore sight;* S, *station for instrument*)

The use of abbreviations as headings is not uncommon and may
be used when making a level book from drawing-paper, providing
that they are understood:

B.S.	= back sight
I.S.	= intermediate sight
F.S.	= fore sight
H. of C.	= height of collimation
R.L.	= reduced level

6.4 CONTINUOUS LEVELLING

When levelling has to extend over a distance outside the range of
the instrument, which can vary but will generally be a maximum of
200 ft, the instrument has to be moved to a number of stations
(Fig. 6.4). The procedure for recording the readings follows the
same pattern from each of the stations.

The instrument is set up at S_1 and a reading is made on the levelling staff held at A; this is a *back sight*. The staff is held at B and a
reading made; this is an *intermediate sight*. The staff is held at C and
a reading made. As it has been decided to move the instrument to
another station, C becomes a *fore sight* and the staff remains at C
until the instrument has been set up at S_2. A reading is then made at
C and this being the *first* reading from S_2 it becomes a *back sight*. For
the extent of the levelling:

A = back sight
B = intermediate sight
C = fore sight and back sight
D = intermediate sight
E = intermediate sight
F = fore sight and back sight
G = fore sight

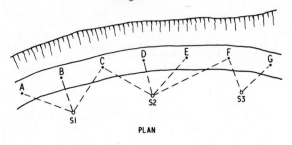

PLAN

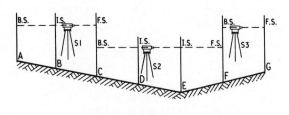

SECTION

Fig. 6.4. Continuous levelling

Because G is the last reading on the sight only one reading is required.

6.5 REDUCED LEVEL

The Reduced Level column in a level book is used to determine the relationship between positions at which readings have been taken and a bench mark or an arbitrary datum.

In all cases the first reduced level opposite position A in the level book must be entered.

If A is a bench mark the correct reduced level is entered. If it is to be an arbitrary datum a reduced level is assumed and this should preferably be a round number such as 50·00 or 100·00 so that conversion later will be made easier.

The remaining readings B to G will then refer to the reduced level at A to provide continuity of the surface being levelled.

The reduced level is the actual level of the surface and readings taken previously are the means by which the reduced level can be obtained.

6.6 RISE-AND-FALL METHOD

A series of readings are taken using three stations and the readings are to be recorded and calculated using the rise-and-fall method (Fig. 6.5).

The positions A to G may be established and measured before levelling commences or each position established just prior to a

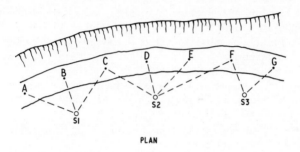

PLAN

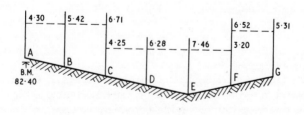

SECTION

Fig. 6.5. Taking readings

reading being taken. The distance between each position is recorded —in this case it is cumulative.

The positions are entered in the Position column if not already printed in the book. The reduced level at position A, in this case a

Table 6.1. CALCULATING THE RISE AND FALL

Position	Distance (ft)	Back Sight	Intermediate Sight	Fore Sight	Rise	Fall	Reduced Level	Remarks
A	0	4·30					82·40	B.M. start
B	50		5·42			1·12		of section
C	100	4·25		6·71		1·29		manhole
D	150		6·28			2·03		
E	200		7·46			1·18		
F	250	6·52		3·20	4·26			
G	300			5·31	1·21			end of section

bench mark, is entered in the Reduced Level column and 'bench mark' recorded in the Remarks column (Table 6.1).

The levelling instrument is set up at $S1$ and a reading taken on the staff held at A. This is found to be 4·30 and is entered in the Back Sight column. The staff is moved to B, the instrument is checked and a reading taken and found to be 5·42. This is entered in the Intermediate Sight column.

The staff is moved to C, the instrument checked and a reading taken and found to be 6·71. This is the last reading from $S1$ and is, therefore, entered in the Fore Sight column.

The levelling staff remains at C and the levelling instrument is moved to $S2$ and set up.

A reading is taken on the staff at C and found to be 4·25. This is the first reading from $S2$ and is entered in the Back Sight column.

The staff is moved to D, the instrument checked and a reading taken and found to be 6·28. This is entered in the Intermediate Sight column.

The staff is moved to E, the instrument checked and a reading taken and found to be 7·46. This is entered in the Intermediate Sight column.

The staff is moved to F, the instrument checked and a reading taken and found to be 3·20. This is the last reading taken from $S2$ and is, therefore, entered in the Fore Sight column.

The levelling staff remains at F and the levelling instrument is moved to $S3$ and set up.

A reading is taken on the staff at F and found to be 6·52. This is the first reading from $S3$ and is entered in the Back Sight column.

The staff is moved to G, the instrument checked and a reading taken and found to be 5·31. This is the last reading in the section and is entered in the Fore Sight column.

The calculations are now made to find the *rise* or the *fall* between the readings by comparing one reading with the preceding reading (Table 6.1).

It must be remembered that the greater reading is a *fall* and the smaller reading is a *rise*.

$$A = 4\cdot30 \quad \text{back sight}$$
$$B = 5\cdot42 \quad \text{intermediate sight}$$

$$1\cdot12 \quad fall$$

$$B = 5\cdot42 \quad \text{intermediate sight}$$
$$C = 6\cdot71 \quad \text{fore sight}$$

$$1\cdot29 \quad fall$$

$$C = 4\cdot25 \quad \text{back sight}$$
$$D = 6\cdot28 \quad \text{intermediate sight}$$

$$2\cdot03 \quad fall$$

$$D = 6\cdot28 \quad \text{intermediate sight}$$
$$E = 7\cdot46 \quad \text{intermediate sight}$$

$$1\cdot18 \quad fall$$

$$E = 7\cdot46 \quad \text{intermediate sight}$$
$$F = 3\cdot20 \quad \text{fore sight}$$

$$4\cdot26 \quad rise$$

$$F = 6\cdot52 \quad \text{back sight}$$
$$G = 5\cdot31 \quad \text{fore sight}$$

$$1\cdot21 \quad rise$$

The difference between B and A is a fall and is entered in the Fall column opposite the position B. The difference between each pair of readings is entered in the appropriate column until all the readings have been covered and in this example will be:

$$B = fall, \quad C = fall, \quad D = fall, \quad E = fall$$
$$F = rise, \quad G = rise$$

6.7 REDUCED LEVEL

The reduced level at position A is a bench mark and its value is known. The value, in this case 82·40, is entered opposite A in the Reduced Level column and 'bench mark' entered in the Remarks column. It is to be remembered that any feature encountered at a position, when levelling, is entered in the Remarks column. In this case a manhole was found at position C (Table 6.2).

In the Remarks column is also entered 'start of section' opposite the position A and 'end of section' opposite position G.

Table 6.2. CALCULATING THE REDUCED LEVEL

Position	Distance (ft)	Back Sight	Intermediate Sight	Fore Sight	Rise	Fall	Reduced Level	Remarks
A	0	4·30					82·40	B.M. start of section
B	50		5·42			1·12	81·28	
C	100	4·25		6·71		1·29	79·99	manhole
D	150		6·28			2·03	77·96	
E	200		7·46			1·18	76·78	
F	250	6·52		3·20	4·26		81·04	
G	300			5·31	1·21		82·25	end of section
		15·07		15·22	5·47	5·62	82·40	= A
				15·07		5·47	82·25	= G
				0·15		0·15	0·15	= fall

The reason for this is to indicate the length of the section which may extend over a few readings entered on one page of the level book or over several pages.

The reduced level at each position other than A has to be established. Because the reduced level is the actual surface where levelling has taken place, it must be appreciated that a *fall* will indicate a *smaller* reduced level and a *rise* will indicate a *higher* reduced level.

Those shown in the Fall column will be subtracted from the previous reduced level and those in the Rise column will be added to the previous reduced level.

To find the reduced levels:

A is known to be   82·40
B = 82·40−1·12 = 81·28
C = 81·28−1·29 = 79·99
D = 79·99−2·03 = 77·96
E = 77·96−1·18 = 76·78
F = 76·78+4·26 = 81·04
G = 81·04+1·21 = 82·25

Each calculated reduced level is entered in this column opposite the appropriate position.

6.8 CHECKING

All entries in a level book should be checked for accuracy of calculations.

Beneath the last entry place in the Reduced Level column the first and last reduced levels and find the difference, in this case:

A = 82·40
G = 82·25

0·15 *fall*

Now find the sum of the Fall column, in this case 5·62. Find the sum of the Rise column, in this case 5·47. Compare the sum of the Rise column to the sum of the Fall column: the answer, in this case 0·15, is the same as the answer for the reduced level as it should be.

To find proof of the calculations, compare the sum of the Back Sight column to the sum of the Fore Sight column and the answer should be identical to the comparison of the Rise column to the Fall column and to that found in the Reduced Level column.

If the answers are not of the same value, an error will be found in the calculations.

Any error that was produced during readings taken on the site cannot be checked by the calculations.

6.9 HEIGHT OF COLLIMATION

The terms 'height of instrument' or 'line of collimation' may sometimes be used to define the height that collimation is above the ground.

Collimation is the sight line produced by viewing through a levelling instrument on to a levelling staff and in this case the term 'height of collimation' will be used.

The procedure for levelling on a site is the same as for the rise-and-fall method but the columns in the level book are set out differently and the method of calculating the reduced level is different.

While the headings for columns in a level book may vary slightly, as do those for the rise-and-fall level book, the main heading will be included.

Similar to the rise-and-fall method the position where the levelling staff is held is entered together with the distance, in this case cumulative, plus the readings obtained for the back sights, intermediate sights and fore sights.

The reduced level at position A is entered together with appropriate remarks in the Remarks column (Table 6.3).

In this case, using the site shown in Fig. 6.5, the height of collimation method is to be used.

The readings are obtained and entered opposite each position in the level book together with the reduced level at A and the appropriate remarks.

The *back sight* reading 4·30 is now *added* to the *reduced level* 82·40:

$$82·40 + 4·30 = 86·70$$

The value 86·70 is the height of collimation at position A and is entered in this column.

Table 6.3. CALCULATING THE REDUCED LEVEL USING THE
HEIGHT OF COLLIMATION METHOD

Position	Distance (ft)	Back Sight	Intermediate Sight	Fore Sight	Height of Collimation	Reduced Level	Remarks
A	0	4·30			86·70	82·40	B.M. start of section
B	50		5·42			81·28	
C	100	4·25		6·71	84·24	79·99	manhole
D	150		6·28			77·96	
E	200		7·46			76·78	
F	250	6·52		3·20	87·56	81·04	
G	300			5·31		82·25	end of section
		15·07		15·22		82·40	= A
				15·07		82·25	= G
				0·15		0·15	= fall

The intermediate sight B is subtracted from the height of collimation to find the reduced level at B:

$$86 \cdot 70 - 5 \cdot 42 = 81 \cdot 28 \text{ R.L. at B}$$

This is then entered in the Reduced Level column.

The fore sight reading at C, 6·71, is now subtracted from the height of collimation, 86·70, to find the reduced level at C:

$$86 \cdot 70 - 6 \cdot 71 = 79 \cdot 99 \text{ R.L. at C}$$

This is then entered in the Reduced Level column.

Because a new station has been used it follows that a new height of collimation must be obtained.

The back sight reading, 4·25, is now added to the reduced level, 79·99:

$$79 \cdot 99 + 4 \cdot 25 = 84 \cdot 24$$

The value 84·24 is the height of collimation to be entered opposite position C.

Calculations follow the same procedure for the remaining reduced levels to position F:

$$D = 84 \cdot 24 - 6 \cdot 28 = 77 \cdot 96 \text{ R.L.}$$
$$E = 84 \cdot 24 - 7 \cdot 46 = 76 \cdot 78 \text{ R.L.}$$
$$F = 84 \cdot 24 - 3 \cdot 20 = 81 \cdot 04 \text{ R.L.}$$

A change of station was made at position F and so a new height of collimation is to be produced by adding the back sight at F to the reduced level at F:

$$81 \cdot 04 + 6 \cdot 52 = 87 \cdot 56 \text{ H of C}$$

and 87·56 is entered in the Height of Collimation column.

The reading at G is the last in the section and is subtracted from 87·56, therefore:

$$87 \cdot 56 - 5 \cdot 31 = 82 \cdot 25 \text{ R.L.}$$

To check the calculations compare the first and last reduced levels, and the sum of the Back Sight column with the sum of the Fore Sight column.

A rule to remember when studying the height of collimation method is: *add* the back sight to produce the height of collimation; *subtract* all other sights to produce the reduced level.

6.10 FLYING LEVELS

After completing a number of readings in detail a check should be made to be certain that the readings are correct.

Flying levels are taken for checking the accuracy of the level readings and this is best done by taking a reading on the bench mark at A, which was the first reading, and another reading at G which was the last reading.

For the purpose of understanding flying levels, a suitable rule is to remember that separate readings are made out of rotation and a comparison made between these and the results obtained from the level book.

Chapter 7

PRODUCING SECTIONS

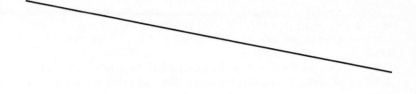

7.1 SECTIONS FROM REDUCED LEVELS

When the reduced levels in a level book have been calculated they indicate the actual level of the surface concerned, in relation to ordnance datum, and while some indication can be obtained about the shape of the surface a sectional drawing will produce a more suitable visual record.

When producing sections two scales are used: *horizontal scale = linear measurement; vertical scale = vertical measurement.*

The vertical scale would normally be about ten times greater than the horizontal scale.

The vertical scale would normally be used to provide a clear indication of the contours of the ground or as a means of being able to provide more suitable detail.

Drawing-paper of a size suitable for the plan and section to be produced is required. It is assumed that the reader is familiar with the necessary equipment and the method used for preparing the drawing-paper.

Decide on the horizontal scale and the vertical scale and enter these near the bottom of the drawing-paper.

Taking the example previously used for levelling (Chapter 6) as the section to be produced, in the top half of the drawing-paper draw a plan of the site, in this case a path 6 ft wide and 300 ft long (Fig. 7.1).

All initial pencil lines produced on the drawing-paper should be fine so that they can be used as the foundation upon which the final work can be superimposed.

Mark on the plan the positions A to G at the distances obtained from the level book, in this case 50 ft intervals.

The plan must represent the true shape of the path throughout its length.

The section drawn in the lower part of the paper is produced from the plan by using the drawing instruments to produce the vertical lines from A, B, C, D, E, F and G on the plan to the section.

Using the line A as the datum, draw horizontal lines at spacings to suit the vertical scale. On the left-hand side of line A enter reduced level values to cover all the reduced levels seen in the level book.

In this case we see that A = 82·40, which is the greatest value, and E = 76·78 which is the smaller value. For the vertical scale on the

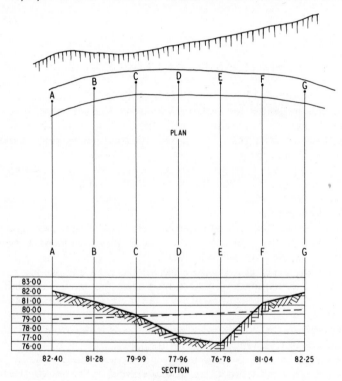

Fig. 7.1. Reduced levels on a site

drawing the reduced levels extend from 76·00 to 83·00 which permit all the reduced levels to be entered for the section.

Using the vertical scale indicated by the reduced levels, use a pencil to indicate the actual reduced level on the vertical lines extending from the plan to the section.

Each of the points are joined by a continuous line and this indicates the true shape of the surface that was levelled.

The boundary lines of the plan and the surface line of the section are the main lines required.

7.2 CUT AND FILL

On examination of the section (Fig. 7.1), it will be seen that the surface falls from A to E and rises from E to G.

When dealing with levelling of the ground prior to excavation work, one of the main objects to economise on site works is to try and produce a balance of the earth excavated and filled because transporting earth off a site or importing it on to a site can be costly.

It will be seen that by drawing a line from 79·50 at A to 80·50 at G, a reasonable balance will be obtained by using the excavation bounded by ABC and FG to fill the low area bounded by CDEF.

Excavation is only one of the items that have to be considered and the actual reduced levels required for a site will naturally depend upon many factors, such as highway surfaces, floor levels, etc.

Chapter 8

TRANSFER OF LEVELS

8.1 ESTABLISHING LEVELS

We have seen that bench marks are permanent marks established by ordnance survey, that a datum is a fixed point upon a surface and that an arbitrary datum is one that is assumed for the purpose of producing level pegs on a site.

The location of a site will determine which method will be used but in all cases the completed levels must eventually refer to the reduced levels that will be provided by ordnance survey.

Buildings are erected perpendicularly and this means that basements and each floor level must be provided at established levels.

Highways are constructed to gradients which enables surface water to drain from them, and as highways are planned as networks it follows that the reduced levels of the channel courses will be related.

Drains and sewers are constructed to gradients that will provide a self-cleansing velocity, and as these are also planned as a network and in some cases with an outfall to tidal waters the reduced levels of the invert of drains and sewers will be related.

When inspecting plans of construction sites, the reduced levels will be indicated at certain places; in the case of a building it may be the ground floor, for a sewer it may be the invert at a manhole and for a highway the channel course at a tangent or at an intersection (Fig. 8.1).

In this example we find that reduced levels have been provided for the highway, sewer and floor level of the buildings and that a bench mark is shown on a gatepost as:

$$\begin{array}{ll}
\text{bench mark} & = 88 \cdot 50 \\
\text{highway channel} & = 86 \cdot 50 \text{ and } 87 \cdot 00
\end{array}$$

sewer invert   = 80·50 and 81·00
building floor levels = 89·00 and 89·50

As the bench mark is adjacent to the site it would be used for the purpose of establishing each of the leveis required but to avoid undue movement from the site to the bench mark a temporary

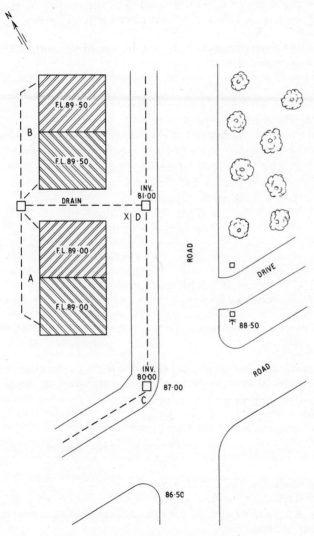

Fig. 8.1. Levels on a site for building and drainage

bench mark may be established at any convenient position, such as X shown on the plan.

The levelling instrument is set up at a convenient position and a levelling staff is held on the bench mark. Assume the reading is found to be 4·20. A stout wooden peg 4 in. by 4 in. is inserted into the ground at X and the levelling staff held on top of this peg.

The peg is driven into the ground until the reading on the staff is seen to be 4·20. Concrete is then placed around the peg to make it secure.

The levelling instrument may now be moved to another position or remain where it is.

Assume it is decided to set up the levelling instrument at a new position and to establish pegs for the buildings.

Set up the levelling instrument and hold the levelling staff on the T.B.M. The reading is found to be 3·65.

Place a peg in the ground at one corner of proposed building A, hold the levelling staff on the peg and adjust the peg until the reading is seen to be 3·15. This is calculated by comparing the difference between the T.B.M. and floor level at A:

$$\text{bench mark} = 88·50; \text{ therefore, T.B.M.} = 88·50$$

$$
\begin{aligned}
\text{T.B.M.} &= 88·50 \\
\text{floor level A} &= 89·00 \\
\hline
&= +\ 0·50
\end{aligned}
$$

$$
\begin{aligned}
\text{Therefore, if T.B.M. reading} &= 3·65 \\
\text{and floor level A} &= 3·15 \\
\hline
\text{plus level} = \text{minus reading} &= 0·50 \text{ difference}
\end{aligned}
$$

To establish a level peg at building B, a peg is placed at the corner of the proposed building and the levelling staff held on this peg.

$$
\begin{aligned}
\text{T.B.M.} &= 88·50 \\
\text{floor level B} &= 89·50 \\
\hline
&= +\ 1·00 = \text{minus reading}
\end{aligned}
$$

The reading at the T.B.M. was 3·65.

The reading for the floor level B = 3·65 − 1·00 = 2·65.

The peg is driven into the ground until the reading on the staff is found to be 2·65.

It will be seen that the invert level of the manholes will be below the T.B.M. In this case a peg is placed in the ground adjacent to the proposed manhole C and at D.

The reading on the levelling staff at the T.B.M. was 3·65 and this represents the reduced level 88·50.

The levelling staff is held on the peg at proposed manhole C and the peg is driven into the ground until the reading on the staff is 4·15 and the peg marked to indicate that it is 8·00 ft above invert level.

The levelling instrument remains in the same position; the levelling staff is moved to the peg at the proposed manhole D.

As the invert level at manhole D is to be 1·00 ft higher than that at manhole C, an attempt should be made to keep this uniformity in levelling. The reading at C was:

$$\begin{array}{r} 4\cdot15 \\ \text{Therefore} \quad -1\cdot00 = \text{rise} \\ \hline \end{array}$$

$$\text{peg D} \quad = 3\cdot15$$

Peg D is 8·00 ft above the proposed invert level of manhole D and this is indicated on the peg.

8.2 USING AN ARBITRARY DATUM

We know that an arbitrary datum is an assumed datum which can be adjusted when the correct reduced level is known (Fig. 8.2).

The plan shows a proposed building, a drain including a manhole and a 300 ft length of highway which is to be set out and levels established. In this case actual reduced levels are not shown but a plus reading is known for the building, a minus reading for the invert at the manhole and the gradient for the highway is also known.

In this case an arbitrary datum is to be used for the channel course at A, and this is given an assumed reduced level of 50·00.

The 300 ft length of new road is set out and pegs placed at B and B'.

The levelling instrument is set up, the levelling staff is held at A and the reading is found to be 6·20; this is recorded.

From A to B is 300 ft and the gradient is rising 1 in 200; this is equal to 1·50.

$$\begin{array}{lll} \text{If A} & = 6\cdot20 = 50\cdot00 & \text{arbitrary datum} \\ \text{rise} & = 1\cdot50- & \\ \hline \text{peg B} & = 4\cdot70 = 51\cdot50 & \\ \hline \end{array}$$

The levelling staff is held on peg B and the peg adjusted until the reading is found to be 4·70 on the staff.

If the channel courses are equal, peg B′ will have the same reading.

Pegs C and D could be produced by means of boning rods but in

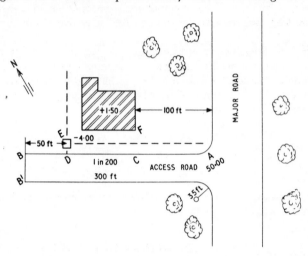

Fig. 8.2. Arbitrary datum

this example all pegs will be produced by means of the levelling instrument set up at one position.

The pegs C and D are now placed according to the measurements with C 100 ft from A, and D 50 ft from B.

From A to C is 100 ft and the gradient is 1 in 200; therefore, the rise is 0·50.

$$\text{The reading at peg A} = 6\cdot20 = 50\cdot00$$
$$\text{rise} \quad = 0\cdot50-$$
$$\text{peg C} = 5\cdot70 = 50\cdot50$$

From A to D is 250 ft and the gradient is 1 in 200; this represents a rise of 1·25.

$$\text{The reading at peg A} = 6\cdot20 = 50\cdot00$$
$$\text{rise} \quad = 1\cdot25-$$
$$\text{peg D} = 4\cdot95 = 51\cdot25$$

It will be noted that the levels A, B, C and D are representing channel courses and in this example the invert level $-4 \cdot 00$ and the floor level for the building $+1 \cdot 50$ are to be taken from the channel levels opposite to them, in this case pegs C and D.

A peg is placed at the position of the proposed manhole, as the channel course will eventually be at a lower level than the manhole cover on top of the manhole. Due allowance is made, in this case $0 \cdot 50$ for the level of the manhole cover.

$$\begin{array}{l} \text{The reading at peg D} = 4 \cdot 95 = 51 \cdot 25 \\ \text{rise} \quad\quad = 0 \cdot 50 - \\ \hline \\ \text{peg E} = 4 \cdot 45 = 51 \cdot 75 \\ \hline \end{array}$$

As the invert at the manhole is to be $4 \cdot 00$ ft below the channel level at D and the top of the manhole cover is to be $0 \cdot 50$ ft above D, this means peg E will be $4 \cdot 50$ ft above the proposed invert level and this is recorded on the peg E for reference.

The peg F is inserted into the ground at the corner of the proposed building. It is known that the floor level represented by peg F is $1 \cdot 50$ ft above the peg C.

$$\begin{array}{l} \text{The reading at peg C} = 5 \cdot 70 = 50 \cdot 50 \\ \text{rise} \quad\quad = 1 \cdot 50 - \\ \hline \\ \text{peg F} = 4 \cdot 20 = 52 \cdot 00 \\ \hline \end{array}$$

To obtain some indication of the relationship between each of the level pegs and the arbitrary datum, they may be compared.

$$\begin{aligned}
A &= 6 \cdot 20; \text{ reading on the staff} = 50 \cdot 00 \\
B &= 4 \cdot 70; \text{ reading on the staff} = 51 \cdot 50 \\
C &= 5 \cdot 70; \text{ reading on the staff} = 50 \cdot 50 \\
D &= 4 \cdot 95; \text{ reading on the staff} = 51 \cdot 25 \\
E &= 4 \cdot 45; \text{ reading on the staff} = 51 \cdot 75 \\
F &= 4 \cdot 20; \text{ reading on the staff} = 52 \cdot 00
\end{aligned}$$

8.3 CONVERTING AN ARBITRARY DATUM

Information regarding the reduced level in relation to ordnance datum will eventually have to be recorded and in this case the difference between the actual reduced levels and the arbitrary ones are subtracted or added as the case may be.

Assume that after establishing the level pegs on the site it becomes known that the actual reduced level at A is $84 \cdot 00$.

Then:

$$
\begin{aligned}
\text{reduced level} &= 84{\cdot}00 \\
\text{arbitrary datum} &= 50{\cdot}00 - \\
\hline
\text{difference} &= 34{\cdot}00
\end{aligned}
$$

The difference in this case is plus and is added to the remaining reduced levels on the site (Table 8.1).

Table 8.1

	Arbitrary Reduced Level	Difference (+)	Actual Reduced Level
A	50·00	34·00	84·00
B	51·50	34·00	85·50
C	50·50	34·00	84·50
D	51·25	34·00	85·25
E	51·75	34·00	85·75
F	52·00	34·00	86·00

8.4 OBSTRUCTION ON THE SITE

When measuring or setting out on a site certain obstructions are often found that would delay work being carried out. It is therefore necessary to know how it is possible to overcome the most common obstructions.

8.4.1 BUILDING

Line AB is the line with A as the working side and B has to be established (Fig. 8.3).

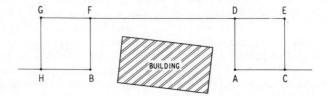

Fig. 8.3. Building obstructs line

A peg is placed at A and another peg C established any reasonable distance from A. Set off right-angles at A and C to establish pegs

D and E clear of the building so that: AC = DE; AD = CE; AE = DC.

Establish pegs G and F any distance to clear the building so that GF = DE.

Set off right-angles to establish pegs H and B, so that: HB = GF; GH = FB; FH = GB.

The pegs BH indicate a continuation of the line AC and the distance DF = AB.

8.4.2 OBSTRUCTED CURVE

Assume, when setting out or measuring a line AB with A the working side, it is possible to sight the line but the measurement cannot be obtained on the site because of an obstruction between A and B,

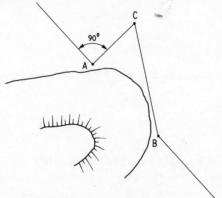

Fig. 8.4. Embankment obstructs line

such as the base of an embankment or a bend in a stream (Fig. 8.4).

Place a ranging pole at A and set off a right-angle to C any distance from A. From C establish B on the known line AB; the measurements AC and CB will be known.

Therefore, $AB^2 = CB^2 - AC^2$, and AB can be calculated.

8.4.3 HIGH WALL

When setting out a straight line on a site, a high wall which may or may not be due for demolition may be found as an obstruction (Fig. 8.5).

If A is the working side and B has to be established, place a peg

at A and C and as a continuation of these pegs place a chalked line
on the wall at X.

Using a straight-edge or ranging pole placed on top of the wall

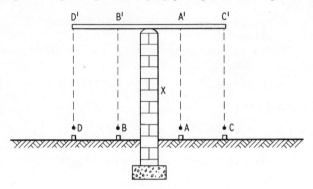

Fig. 8.5. High wall obstructs line

at X, suspend plumb bobs C', A', B' and D' with A' over A and
C' over C.

Secure the straight-edge and place pegs at B under B' and D
under D'.

The pegs BD will be a continuation of line AC.

8.4.4 CUTTING

Existing cuttings or those made by mechanical plant on a site may
obstruct measurement although vision is not obstructed.

If AB is the unknown measurement and A the working side, set
off C at right-angles to AX any distance and erect a ranging pole
(Fig. 8.6).

Establish $D = \frac{1}{2} AC$ and erect a ranging pole so that ranging
poles are erected at A, B, C, and D.

An assistant holds a ranging pole at E which must be at right-
angles to AC.

Sighting from B through D signal for E to be moved into line;
the angle ACE must be maintained.

The measurement CE = unknown measurement AB.

8.4.5 SLOPING GROUND

It is sometimes necessary to determine the horizontal measurement
of steep sloping ground on a site (Fig. 8.7).

Take A as the top of the slope, measure horizontally a convenient

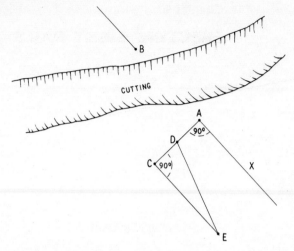

Fig. 8.6. Cutting obstructs line

distance AB and establish C using a drop arrow or plumb bob. Measure CD and establish E; measure EF and establish G which is the bottom of the slope.

The cumulative total: AB + CD + EF = horizontal measurement AG.

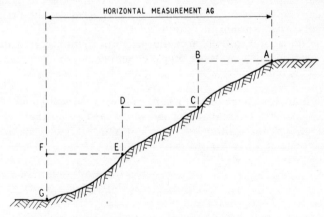

Fig. 8.7. Measuring sloping land

Chapter 9

ERECTING SIGHT RAILS

9.1 SIGHT RAILS

When it is required to maintain uniformity of levels on a site for the purpose of producing a level surface, a crossfall or a gradient, it is necessary to provide something that can be identified and used by the site foreman.

Sight rails provide the means by which the foreman is able to control work where levelling is his concern. The sight rails may vary in shape according to the work they are serving but basically all sight rails contain a horizontal rail supported by one or more uprights firmly set into the ground.

The horizontal rail which is the sight rail should be of 4 in. by 1 in. or 6 in. by 1 in. thick prepared timber, nailed or preferably screwed to one or more wooden uprights of not less than 4 in. by 3 in. section.

It is an advantage to paint sight rails with vertical bands about 6 in. wide, using alternate black and white bands as an aid to identification, both for sighting purposes and also as a guide for drivers of transport and plant on the site.

9.2 WIDE EXCAVATIONS

Excavations required for work ·concerned with highways, large buildings, etc., where sight rails have to be placed to cover an area square or rectangular in shape, would normally have a number of sight rails to permit transverse, longitudinal and diagonal levelling.

It is not advisable to use wooden pegs, for setting out work, which also serve as level pegs. While level pegs can be used for certain works, and when they are they should preferably be painted white, the tendency on sites is for setting out pegs to be knocked over, particularly on the blind sides of machines.

If pegs are used to control alignment and level, they should be placed with some clearance from the edge of excavation.

When using this method for excavating, the pegs should be placed about 2 ft outside the line of excavation. If possible the top of the peg should denote a datum, but if this is not possible because of undulating ground a mark should be placed on the side of the peg using an etched line or a mark made by waterproof crayon. A nail is driven into the side of the peg and an arrowhead drawn on the side of the peg to indicate the level.

If excavation is to be 2 ft below the level, a wooden template used as a gauge is made. This is carried on the excavating machine or by a responsible person on the site.

To obtain information about the level of the formation in relation to the level peg the template is placed with one arm touching the

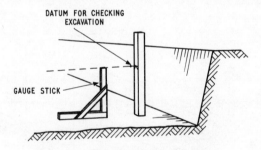

Fig. 9.1. Using gauge stick for control of excavation

excavation and the other extended to the peg. From this it is possible to obtain a reasonable guide but final trimming later would normally have to be made to meet the tolerances provided in a specification (Fig. 9.1).

More suitable control of excavation can be obtained by erecting sight rails at level pegs so that the horizontal rail is a known height above the pegs, which are all uniform, to permit the use of a boning rod or a travelling rod.

Assume formation level is to be 2 ft below a level peg and this requires 1 ft 6 in. of excavation.

A convenient height above the ground for sighting is taken as 3 ft and this allows for using a boning rod 4 ft 6 in. long. A wooden upright of about 3 in. by 3 in. section is driven into the ground without disturbing the level peg if this has been established.

The distance 3 ft is measured up the side of the upright and a line marked.

The horizontal rail of 3 in. by $\frac{1}{2}$ in. or 4 in. by $\frac{1}{2}$ in. section timber is screwed or nailed to the upright and the top of this rail checked by means of a spirit-level.

The horizontal sight rail should be placed parallel to the line of the excavation. This permits transverse and diagonal levelling to be carried out and provides the least possible obstruction for machines moving on the site.

9.3 CUTTINGS

Excavations of considerable depth often have to be carried out and in this case the normal method of setting out and levelling is not suitable.

Excavating cuttings does not permit the use of timbering, as in the case of trenchworks; consequently it is necessary to know the

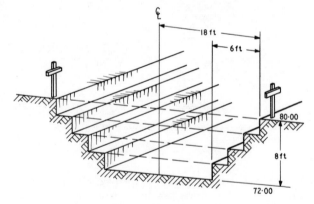

Fig. 9.2. Excavating cuttings

angle of repose of the earth being excavated so that the sides of the cutting can remain safe.

Assume a carriageway is to be constructed on a formation level of 72·00 and the ground level is 80·00. This allows for 8 ft depth of excavation (Fig. 9.2).

The angle of repose of the earth is known to be 45°.

The centre line pegs are set out and offset pegs fixed on each side to allow for construction + working + angle of repose. This would be 10 ft+2 ft+6 ft = 18 ft. The outside pegs when set out would provide for a cut 36 ft wide at the ground level.

If a scraper is used for excavation the earth would be cut in a series of steps which enables the width of the cutting to be reduced to the formation, which is 24 ft wide.

On completion of the excavation both sides of the cutting are trimmed by means of a grader or by manual labour.

To control the levels for the excavation, sight rails are placed near the outside pegs at ground level and a boning rod or travelling rod used in the cutting.

Deep cuttings can be controlled by using two sets of sight rail, one set at ground level and a second set on one of the treads about half way down the sides of the cutting.

When fixing the lower set of sight rails it is a simple matter to subtract the difference in height between the two from the total depth of the cut.

9.4 LEVELLING THE EARTHWORKS

Mechanical plant used for earth moving are able to work to reasonably accurate formations but when excavating cuttings or forming embankments one has to resort to manual labour if grading machines

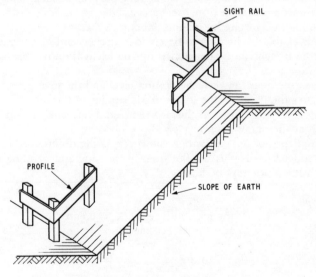

Fig. 9.3. Levelling embankments

capable of being preset to required slopes are not available.

Sight rails and profiles combined are normally used to control the work of trimming and levelling the earth (Fig. 9.3).

The sight rail is erected at the top and the foot of the slope 2–3 ft above ground level. A second arm is provided with the sight rail; this is the profile.

The profile at the top of the slope is fixed at the required angle of slope downwards and the one at the foot of the slope is fixed at the required angle of slope upwards. A string line extended from one to the other will indicate the angle of the slope as a parallel line from which the earth can be controlled as it is being levelled and graded.

9.5 SIGHT RAILS FOR TRENCHWORKS

Drains and sewers are normally constructed in open trenches when they are less than 15 ft below the ground level. To be able to transfer the alignment of a drain or the level of its invert to the depth required, sight rails are normally used.

For this type of work the sight rails are erected to span the width of the trench before or after excavation has been carried out.

Wherever possible the manhole shafts would be excavated at each end of a section, using a machine such as a back acter or a multi-purpose machine to excavate as low as possible with final trimming being done by manual labour.

This enables sight rails to be erected at each end of a section so that the trench can be controlled during excavation by means of a travelling rod.

The difference between the ground level and the invert level at A indicates the depth of the lower inside surface of the pipe.

The difference between the two reduced levels at B indicates the depth at the opposite end.

The depth of the excavation, however, is the difference between the reduced levels plus the thickness of the pipe and bedding upon which the pipes may be laid.

Example

$$
\begin{array}{ll}
\text{If the ground level at A} & = \; 80\cdot00 \\
\text{and the invert level} & = \; 73\cdot00 \\
\hline
\text{depth to invert} & = \quad 7\cdot00 \\
\end{array}
$$

Therefore, if the thickness of the pipe and the bedding combined was 6 in. ($= 0\cdot50$) the depth of excavation would be:

$$7\cdot00 + 0\cdot50 = 7\cdot50 \text{ ft (Fig. 9.4)}$$

Drains and sewers are constructed to gradients that will provide a self-cleansing velocity such as a flow of 3 ft per second. The level of the ground at the top of a trench will not normally have the same contours or gradient and this means that the trench may be deeper at one end than the other.

By erecting sight rails at each end of a section taken as 200 ft, which is a reasonable sighting distance, the uniformity of formation

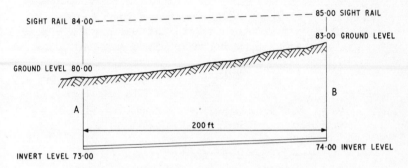

Fig. 9.4. Relationship between ground level and invert level

at the bottom of the trench is ensured. If this distance is too great for accurate levelling, intermediate sight rails are erected.

If the depth of trench at A	=	7·50 ft
and at B the ground level	=	83·00
and invert level	=	74·00
depth to invert	=	9·00
+ thickness of pipe and bedding	=	0·50
depth of excavation at B	=	9·50 ft

Sight rails should be placed at reasonable heights above ground level to enable sighting to be carried out when standing on the ground. Heights varying from 3 ft to 5 ft above ground level are normally suitable.

If a sight rail is erected at A 4 ft above ground level (= 84·00), this will be 11 ft above the invert level. The drain is known to have a fall of 1 ft from B to A = 74·00 − 73·00 = 1·00 ft. Therefore, the sight rail erected at B will be 84·00 + 1·00 = 85·00.

The ground level at B is known to be 83·00; therefore,

$$85·00 = \text{sight rail}$$
$$83·00 = \text{ground level}$$

$$\text{sight rail} = \quad 2·00 \quad \text{above ground level}$$

To check the accuracy of this a comparison is made between invert level and sight rail level at A, and invert level and sight rail level at B.

$$A = \text{sight rail} \quad 84·00$$
$$ \text{invert level} \quad 73·00$$

$$\text{difference} \quad = \quad 11·00$$

$$B = \text{sight rail} \quad 85·00$$
$$ \text{invert level} \quad 74·00$$

$$\text{difference} \quad = \quad 11·00$$

This means that the sight rail is 11 ft above the invert level at A and also 11 ft above the invert level at B.

A travelling rod 11 ft long may be used to establish the accuracy of the pipes as they are laid in this section (Fig. 9.4).

9.6 STEPPED SIGHT RAILS

When the ground is undulating or falling to the extent that a number of sight rails would be too high above the ground, or in some cases

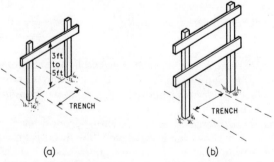

(a)   (b)

Fig. 9.5. (a) Single sight rail; (b) stepped or double sight rails

too low, taking 3–5 ft as reasonable heights for sighting purposes, the method known as stepping is used (Fig. 9.5).

Using the example shown, the sight rails at A, A³ and B would be single; those in between would be double (Fig. 9.6).

When erecting the sight rails on the site it must be possible to sight from A to A¹, A¹ to A², A² to A³, A³ to A⁴, A⁴ to A⁵ and A⁵ to B, and vice versa. When using this method it is necessary to use a travelling rod of varying length and it is important that the appropriate length of traveller be recorded on the sighting side of the sight rail.

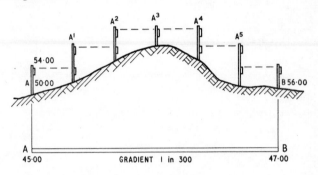

Fig. 9.6. *Using stepped sight rails*

Instead of having a number of travelling rods on the site a single one with a staff of suitable length and section with a movable traveller is suitable; this enables the traveller to be moved up or down the staff to be secured at the appropriate measurement (Fig. 9.7).

To set up the stepped sight rails, assuming A is the working side, note the invert level at A and B and it will be seen that the drain has a fall of 2 ft from B to A. As the gradient is shown to be 1 in 300, this means that the distance from A to B is 300 × 2 = 600 ft.

The ground is undulating and sight rails will be required more frequently. Set up the sight rail at A, 4 ft above ground level; 50·00 + 4·00 = 54·00 sight rail.

Measure horizontally over the ground 100 ft and erect sight rail uprights A¹. Transfer the reading obtained with a levelling instrument at A to the uprights at A¹; raise this height 4 in. (1 in 300 at 100 ft); mark the uprights and fix the sight rail accurately.

Measure on the uprights 2 ft above the sight rail and fix the second sight rail at A¹ (the actual measurement used between the two sight rails will depend upon the contours of the ground).

Measure horizontally over the ground 100 ft and erect sight rail uprights A^2. Transfer the reading obtained on the top sight rail at A^1 to the uprights at A^2 and fix the sight rail 4 in. above this (Fig. 9.8).

Measure on the uprights 2 ft above the sight rail and fix the second sight rail at A^2. Establish uprights at A^3 and transfer the reading obtained on the top sight rail at A^2 to A^3 and raise this 4 in.; fix the sight rail at A^3.

In this example it is found that a single rail is suitable at A^3 and

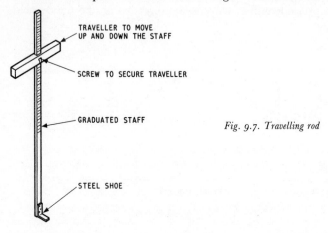

TRAVELLER TO MOVE
UP AND DOWN THE STAFF

SCREW TO SECURE TRAVELLER

GRADUATED STAFF

STEEL SHOE

Fig. 9.7. Travelling rod

this height can be transferred to the uprights set up at A^4 and raised 4 in. The ground is now found to be falling; therefore, the next sight rail at A^4 will be 1 ft lower. This is transferred to the uprights at A^5 and raised 4 in. As the ground starts to rise again the second

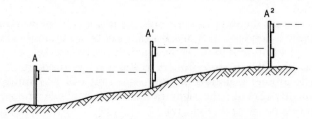

Fig. 9.8. Setting up stepped sight rails

sight rail at A^5 is 2 ft lower and this is transferred to the single sight rail at B and raised 4 in.

The length of travelling rod required for each set of sight rails must be calculated and recorded on each appropriate sight rail so that a uniform gradient of 1 in 300 can be obtained.

With A as the working side:

A to A^1 = 50·00 ground level
            45·00 invert level
            _____
            5·00
         + 2·00 sight rail above ground
            _____
            7·00 ft = length of travelling rod
            _____

A^1 to A^2 = 7·00 ft
            + 2·00 top sight rail above lower sight rail
            _____
            9·00 ft = length of travelling rod
            _____

A^2 to A^3 = 9·00
            + 2·00 top sight rail above lower sight rail
            _____
            11·00 ft = length of travelling rod
            _____

A^3 to A^4 = 11·00
            + 0·00
            _____
            11·00 ft = length of travelling rod
            _____

A^4 to A^5 = 11·00
            − 1·00 lower sight rail below top sight rail
            _____
            10·00 ft = length of travelling rod
            _____

A^5 to B = 10·00
            − 2·00 lower sight rail below top sight rail
            _____
            8·00 ft = length of travelling rod
            _____

It must be appreciated that when trenches are manually excavated the sight rails may span the proposed trench but when a
mechanical appliance is to be used the sight rails have to be erected
at one side of the proposed trench to permit the machine to work.
The position of the sight rails will be influenced by the method

to be used for excavating and this information must be available
before levelling commences.

9.7 USING SIGHT RAILS

A standard rule cannot be laid down that it is more suitable to
sight over the rails from the lower one to the higher one, or vice
versa, because site conditions can influence which will be most
suitable.

Drains and sewer pipes would normally be laid in a trench from
the lower end so that work progresses up gradient mainly because
water that does gain access to the trench will flow away from the
construction work. If the pipes are being laid from an existing manhole the water in the trench will flow from the new construction
and into the existing sewer.

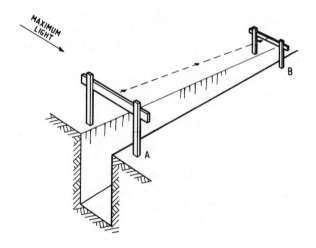

Fig. 9.9. Using sight rails

One of the main considerations to obtain efficiency when using
sight rails is to allow the maximum light and most suitable background for the sight rail on to which a sight is being made. This
applies particularly in the case of strong sunshine, in which case it
is often found more suitable to have the sun shining from A to B
with a sight line being made from A to B (Fig. 9.9).

A drain or sewer is designed so that the gradient will provide a
self-cleansing velocity which makes the accuracy of the invert level

important. A plus or minus deviation from accuracy can result in loss of the self-cleansing velocity in a section of the work.

If the sight rails and travelling rod are not used as a means of checking every pipe that is laid, a fall board made to suit the actual

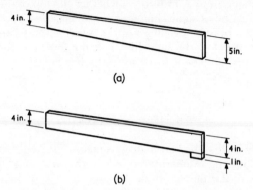

Fig. 9.10. (a) Correct fall board; (b) temporary fall board

fall over a short distance such as 3 ft must be used for checking the accuracy of the pipes between those checked by using the sight rails (Fig. 9.10).

The advantage of using a fall board is that accuracy is checked

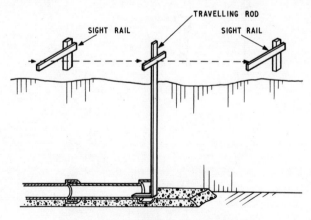

Fig. 9.11. Using sight rails and travelling rod

as a pipe is laid and does not entail waiting for a sight to be taken over sight rails.

It must be considered important that periodic checks be made using the sight rails and travelling rod whether a fall board is, or is not, used.

The steel toe of the travelling rod is held on the invert of the pipe having ascertained that the correct travelling rod is being used. A sight is made from A to B to see whether the top of the travelling rod is on the line of sight (Fig. 9.11).

If the top of the travelling rod is above the sight line the invert is too high, if below the sight line, it is too low, and the necessary adjustment to the pipe is made until the line of sight is found to be accurate.

9.8 DEEP TRENCHES

When pipes have to be laid in deep trenches where the use of a very long travelling rod is found unsuitable, sight rails would be replaced by a series of datums established in the trench, so that when the

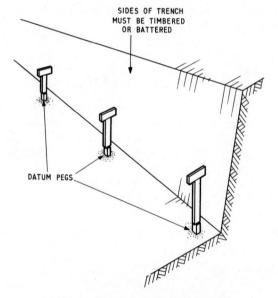

Fig. 9.12. Using boning rods in trenches

pipes are laid a check is carried out using a set of boning rods (Fig. 9.12).

It is necessary to fix a datum that will represent the invert level at a manhole shaft and this must be firmly established by using an engineering brick or a flat piece of natural stone set in concrete.

From this datum a number of wooden pegs may be placed at intervals throughout the trench.

The drainlayer sets out his line in the normal way and using a set of standard boning rods levelling continues throughout the length of the trench.

Although a travelling rod may be considered to be too long for general use, one should be available for periodic checking of the invert of the drain because of possible error that may occur over long distances when using boning rods for this type of work.

9.9 OPEN CUTTINGS

It is sometimes more convenient to excavate open cuttings with a shallow trench at the bottom for the purpose of constructing a drain or sewer (Fig. 9.13).

This method may be used where space is available, the earth is workable and mechanical plant suitable for the excavation can be employed.

The open cut is excavated and sight rails provided using the same

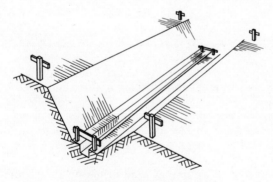

Fig. 9.13. Sight rails for open cuttings

method explained earlier in this chapter under the heading 'Cuttings' (Section 9.3).

The trench at the bottom of the cutting would not normally exceed about 4 ft depth and the side haunches about 3–4 ft wide.

This method would normally be used where the ground is of low load-bearing capacity; an open cut is more acceptable than close timbering and the method is not detrimental to construction at ground level.

To control levelling in the trench at the bottom of the cutting, sight rails are set up as for normal trenchworks by transferring the required reduced level from ground level.

9.10 HEADINGS

When construction work, particularly in the case of sewers, has to be executed and where the depth to the invert indicates that it is more economical to tunnel through the ground, or the nature of the ground indicates that it would be more suitable to provide a

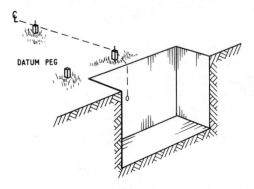

Fig. 9.14. Transfer of centre line down shaft

tunnel in which construction can be carried out, a heading is driven through the earth without disturbing it at ground level.

Similarly, headings may have to be provided under railways or busy highways to prevent creating a hazard for traffic.

Some part of the setting out and levelling has to be done above ground as well as in the heading as a check on the accuracy of the work.

To commence a heading at a given datum the alignment is set out by means of wooden pegs at ground level.

The shaft is excavated using the necessary safety precautions. A strong setting out line with a suspended plumb bob is extended from the centre line pegs to the shaft and lowered accordingly as excavation is carried out. This enables the centre line to be continued on one wall to the bottom of the shaft (Fig. 9.14).

A datum peg will be situated at the top of the shaft from which vertical measurements can be obtained. A steel tape or measuring rod is extended from the datum peg to the bottom of the shaft until the required depth (depth of excavation + thickness of pipe + bed) has been produced.

In most cases a shaft excavated in earth will require timbering
for reasons of safety, and as timbering proceeds so the centre line
is marked by means of chalk or waterproof crayon on the surface
of the timbering.

When a shaft has been excavated to the required depth, a datum
is established at formation level. As considerable activity will
be taking place at the bottom of the shaft the datum from which
levelling will be continued throughout the heading must be firm
without being an obstruction.

A flat-surfaced piece of natural stone, such as 'York' stone, or a

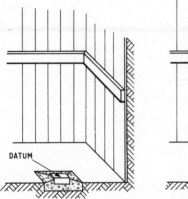

Fig. 9.15. Datum at bottom of shaft   Fig. 9.16. Datum on wall of shaft

blue engineering brick placed at the invert level, bedded and
surrounded with concrete, that is ramped down to the formation
level, will normally be suitable (Fig. 9.15).

When this method of establishing a datum is not suitable a datum
is provided on the side of the shaft by cutting an arrowhead with a
surmounted line, with the line representing a height 1 ft above the
invert and this is indicated at the side of the datum (Fig. 9.16).

To commence excavating the heading mark is cut into the side
of the shaft where the plumb line is suspended. The size for the
heading is marked upon the earth and an opening is made.

A second plumb line is now suspended down the side of the shaft
opposite to the first plumb line and a small illumination provided
at the rear of the plumb bob at a height convenient for sighting.

As excavation continues for the heading the centre line is
transferred to the working face by sighting along the two plumb
bobs and inserting into the roof of the heading metal dogs to which
a string line is attached (Fig. 9.17).

Any deviation in alignment or in the level of the formation can be costly because of the methods that have to be adopted for excavating headings. It is therefore worthwhile establishing metal dogs for the centre line at frequent intervals and at the same time

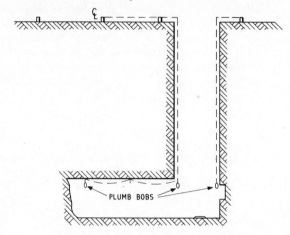

Fig. 9.17. Transfer of centre line for heading

establish level pegs painted white to indicate the formation level for the heading and a measuring rod to assist in gauging a uniform height throughout.

If the datum established at the bottom of the shaft indicates the invert level of the sewer or whatever the heading is being used for, the formation level for the heading must include the thickness of pipe + thickness of bed.

To transfer the levels from the shaft to the working face any one of a number of methods may be used (Fig. 9.18).

A Cowley automatic levelling instrument is suitable because of its size. A dumpy level is also suitable but in a small heading a folding staff is more convenient than a telescopic staff.

For intermediate levelling a set of boning rods would be suitable but when using this method some extra illumination must be provided at the working face or back-boning may be made from the working face towards the shaft using the light at the shaft as the background.

To a more limited extent a fall board of not less than 6 ft length may be used, but in this case a periodic check must be carried out by using a levelling instrument.

When the formation level has been established wooden pegs are placed at uniform spacings to indicate invert levels. Where the

earth is too hard to accept pegs it is advisable to use natural stone
or engineering bricks set in concrete to indicate levels at the required
intervals.

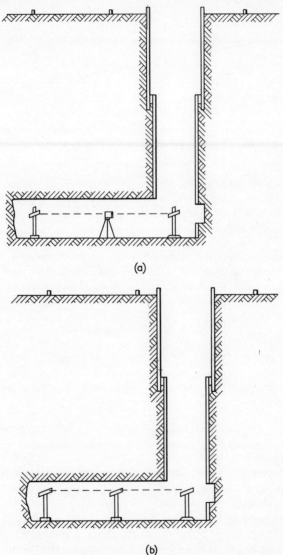

(a)

(b)

Fig. 9.18. Minor levelling in headings: (a) using the Cowley automatic
level in small headings with suitable light for levelling; (b) using
boning rods for levelling

Chapter 10

CURVES

The method used for setting out curves and establishing levels on the curvature provided will be influenced by the length of the radius from which the curve is produced, which in turn will influence the length of the curve.

A curve may be described as an arc of the circumference of a circle which could be produced by a radius. All curves, however, are not designed from one radius; in some cases, three may be used.

When a curve is designed from a single radius it is sometimes referred to as a simple curve; when a number of radii are used it is a

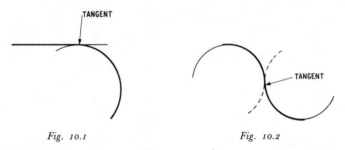

Fig. *10.1*   Fig. *10.2*

compound curve or a transition curve. When a curve consists of two arcs produced from centres at opposite sides it is referred to as a reverse curve or an ogee curve.

Curves may be defined by the length of the radius or by degrees indicating the angle from which the curve is produced. No matter which method is used to define a curve, it is important that the straight line must be a tangent to the curve (Fig. 10.1).

When more than one curve is to be set out each must be tangential to the other (Fig. 10.2).

A simple curve is used for numerous construction designs and apart from sewers, tunnels, highways and railways the radius will often be 100 ft long or less.

Providing that space is available on the site for setting out a curve from the inside, simple curves of 100 ft radius and less can be set out from an established centre using a measuring tape or chain.

The following terms associated with curves should be learnt and remembered (Fig. 10.3):

A = apex: produced by the continuation of the straight lines.
C = long chord: normally extending between tangents.
C^1 = short chord: cutting any two points on a curve.
S = straight lines: terminating at the tangents when a curve has been set out.
T = tangent: the point where a curve joins the straight line.
V = major offset: sometimes referred to as the 'versed sine' and extends from the long chord to the curve.
R = radius: extending from the centre to the tangent.
O = centre: sometimes referred to as the pivot.

It is not intended in this book to deal with the subject of curve ranging which can be studied from well-established books dealing

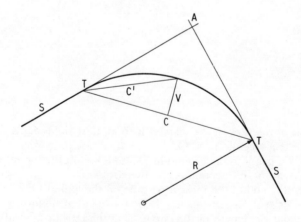

Fig. 10.3. Terms used for curves

with this subject. It is intended, however, to introduce to the reader some of the most common curves, how to produce them on a site and how to establish levels for curves.

10.1 SIMPLE CURVE

We know that a simple curve will have a common radius but must understand that this can vary considerably; for setting out the curve using a measuring tape or a chain using a centre it should have a radius of 100 ft or less.

Assume a curve is to have a radius of 35 ft and is to join straight lines set out at right-angles to each other (Fig. 10.4).

Let S be the straight lines, with T and T^1 as the tangents and A the apex.

Measure $A-T = 35$ ft; measure $A-T^1 = 35$ ft.

Place the end of a measuring tape at T, extend the tape to 35 ft and at right-angles to ST, strike an arc on the ground at O. Place

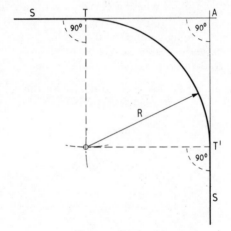

Fig. 10.4. Simple curve

the end of the tape at T^1, extend it to 35 ft at right-angles to ST^1 and strike a second arc at O.

Insert a peg into the ground at O and a nail in the top of the peg at the point of intersection of the two arcs.

Place the end of the measuring tape on the nail at O, extend the tape to 35 ft so that it touches T. Set out pegs at uniform spacings throughout the length of the curve using the tape as the radius.

It is sometimes necessary to set out a curve of known radius and to establish the tangents when two lines such as a wall or kerbline have been set out at an acute angle [Fig. 10.5(a)].

The lines A and C, which are the straight lines set out, are extended to B, in this case the apex. The resulting angle is then bisected to produce line BD.

The known radius R^1 is set off at right-angles to line A (or C) and is shown as EF. The line R^2 is set off at any distance parallel to R^1 and is shown as GH.

The line FH is then produced to cut the line BD at O. The required radius is shown as R^3 with centre at O. A peg with a nail

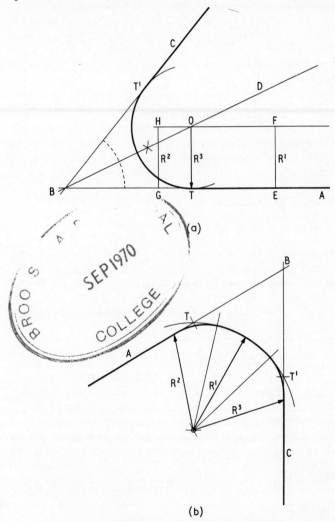

(a)

(b)

Fig. 10.5. Simple curve with tangential curves: (a) curve of known radius at acute angle; (b) because R^1 is not tangential to T and T^1, a tangential curve R^2 is required to ease R^1 into A at T and R^3 into C at T^1

inserted into the top is placed at O. The measuring tape is placed over the nail and the tape extended as R^3 to the line AB to produce the tangent T.

The tape is now moved to the line BC to establish the second tangent T^1. Pegs are placed at the two tangents and further pegs placed throughout the curve.

If the curve is to be produced from a known centre which will not permit the curve to be tangential to the lines A and C, the curve is set out, and in this case a tangential curve would have to be produced as R^2 to ease the curve into A at T and another used as R^3 to ease the curve into C at T^1 [Fig. 10.5(b)].

10.2 LARGE CURVE

A curve designed with a radius greater than 100 ft may be set out by using a system of chords and offsets and this method is suitable whether the curve has to be set out inside or outside because of some obstruction or not.

The formula for finding the first offset is:

$$O^1 = \frac{C^2}{2R} \text{ and } O^1 \times 2 = O^2$$

where C is the chord, R the radius, O^1 the first offset, and O^2 the remaining offsets.

A final adjustment may have to be made at the final offset to ease

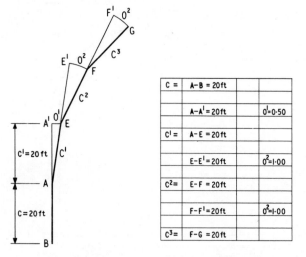

C =	A–B = 20 ft	
	A–A^1 = 20 ft	O^1=0·50
C^1 =	A–E = 20 ft	
	E–E^1 = 20 ft	O^2=1·00
C^2=	E–F = 20 ft	
	F–F^1=20 ft	O^2=1·00
C^3=	F–G = 20 ft	

Fig. 10.6. Setting out large curves using a measuring tape

the curve to the tangent but with practice a suitable curve can be produced.

Assume a curve of 400 ft radius is to be set out and a chord 20 ft long has been chosen (Fig. 10.6):

As O^1 $= \dfrac{C^2}{2R}$

then O^1 $= \dfrac{20 \times 20}{2 \times 400} = \dfrac{400}{800} = \dfrac{1}{2} = 0.50 = 6$ in.

If $O^1 \times 2$ $= O^2$

then $0.50 \times 2 = 1.00 = 1$ ft

therefore, $O^1 = 6$ in. and $O^2 = 12$ in.

Assume AB is the straight line with A the tangent. Measure $A–A^1 = 20$ ft as a continuation of AB, measure the offset $O^1 = \frac{1}{2}$ ft from A^1 to E and fix a peg.

Measure 20 ft from E to E^1 as a continuation of AE, measure the offset $O^2 = 1$ ft from E^1 to F and fix a peg.

Measure 20 ft from F to F^1 as a continuation of EF, measure the offset $O^2 = 1$ ft from F^1 to G and fix a peg.

The pegs A, E, F and G represent the curve.

10.3 CHORDS AND OFFSETS

A method that may be used for setting out a small curve or any part of a large curve is by using a number of offsets from a chord of known length (Fig. 10.7).

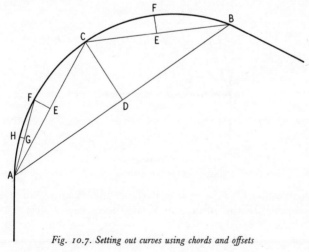

Fig. 10.7. Setting out curves using chords and offsets

The tangents A and B have been established and AB measured.
Halve the chord AB to find D ($\frac{1}{2}$ AB = AD).

The offset D–C is known and a peg is placed at C at right-angles
to AD.

The chord AC is measured which should equal BC.

Halve the chord AC to find E ($\frac{1}{2}$ AC = AE), similarly $\frac{1}{2}$ BC = BE.

The offset EF is calculated by dividing CD by 4 and the result is
used to measure the offset EF at right-angles to AE.

Establish G by $\frac{1}{2}$ AF = AG and calculate GH by FE ÷ 4, set off
H from G at right-angles to AG and fix a peg.

Continue to halve the chord and quarter the previous offset
to establish pegs for the curve.

It is a matter of opinion what measurement the smallest offset
should be to produce a suitable curve. In practice it will normally
be found that if the smallest offset is measured as 1 in., this is suitable
for small curves, while a 2 in. offset is suitable for large curves.

10.4 ORDINATES FROM CHORD

It is sometimes necessary to set out curves when the radius is known,
the tangents are fixed but the main offset is not known and the centre
O is not accessible (Fig. 10.8).

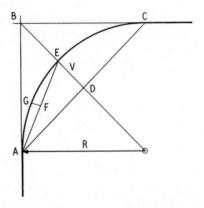

Fig. 10.8. Ordinates from chords

Assume that O is the centre, R the radius, A and C the tangents,
B the apex, DE the offset, and V the rise or versed sine.
Then:

$$OD^2 = OA - AD^2 = R^2 - (\tfrac{1}{2}AC)^2$$

and

$$OD = \sqrt{R^2 - (\tfrac{1}{2}AC)^2}$$
$$V = R - \sqrt{R^2 - (\tfrac{1}{2}AC)^2}$$

With the offset DE = V, this is set out at right-angles to AD and a peg placed at E.

Measure the chord AE and establish F = $\tfrac{1}{2}$ AE. The offset is now produced by using the method dealt with for chords and offsets and a number of pegs produced to determine the curve by using the chord and offset method.

It is also possible to set out pegs to represent the curve by calculating lengths of ordinates from the long chord.

10.5 REVERSE OR OGEE CURVE

The reverse curve consists of two curves and has three tangents. Two tangents are used where the curves join the straight lines and a third tangent is used where the two separate curves join (Fig. 10.9).

Assume X is the distance between the tangents representing the

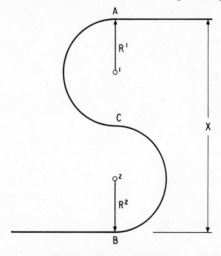

Fig. 10.9. Reverse or ogee curve

straight lines, the distance X = $(R^1 \times 2) + (R^2 \times 2)$ and $R^1 = AO^1$; AC = $2R^1$; CB = $2R^2$, with ACB in line, as $R^1 = \tfrac{1}{2}$ AC.

Set off O^1 at right-angles to A and set out a curve (180°) terminating at C.

As $R^2 = \tfrac{1}{2}$ CB.

Set off O² at right-angles to B and set out a curve (180°) terminating at C.

10.6 LEVELLING FOR CURVES

Only the elements of levelling for curves that will be found on many construction sites can be covered here. Levelling for vertical curves, superelevation and spiral curves is a lengthy subject for which some well-known books have been published.

The normal levelling consists of transferring reduced level pegs from tangents and throughout the curve.

Where the tangent pegs and the curve have the same reduced level throughout it is simply a matter of setting up a levelling instrument,

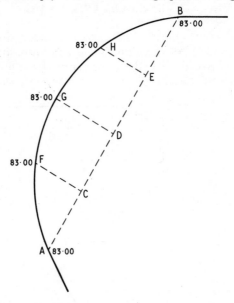

Fig. 10.10. Levelling for curves

establishing or checking the tangent pegs A and B and then transferring the readings to pegs F, G and H on the curve (Fig. 10.10).

When a levelling instrument is not available and boning rods with straight-edge and spirit-level have to be used, the pegs can be established by producing the chord AB and dividing this to provide a number of ordinates CF, DG and EH.

Boning rods are used to establish level pegs at C, D and E from

A and B and a straight-edge and spirit-level used to transfer C to F, D to G and E to H.

Accuracy in the use of equipment is naturally essential.

It may sometimes be found that one tangent is higher than the other (Fig. 10.11).

In this example, B is 1·00 higher than A and a uniform fall is required throughout the curve.

If the chord AB is produced and divided into a number of equal parts, in this example four parts to produce pegs at C, D and E, a

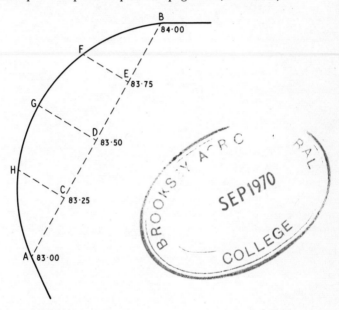

Fig. 10.11. Levelling for curves

transfer of levels on this chord will result as C = 83·25, D = 83·50 and E = 83·75.

These levels would then be transferred at ordinates CH, DG and EF to produce pegs at HG and F.

It will be seen that the difference between A and C = 0·25 on the chord and when C is transferred to H the difference in level between AH will be less than AC because of the length of the curve.

When three or more reduced levels are found on a curve each pair of levels must be treated separately (Fig. 10.12):

$$A = 84·00 \quad C = 84·50 = 0·50 \text{ difference}$$
$$C = 84·50 \quad B = 83·75 = 0·75 \text{ difference}$$

In this case A and C would be used to produce D and any intermediate levels, while C and B would be used to produce E and any
intermediate levels.

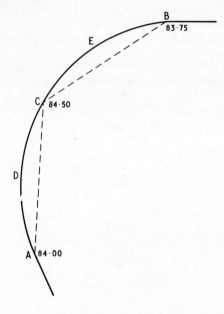

Fig. 10.12. Levelling for curves

Chapter 11

CONTOURS

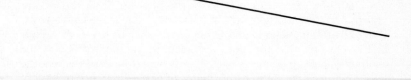

Contours are undulations of a surface such as the earth's and contour lines are imaginary lines indicating the rise and fall of the surface.

Contour lines, normally red or brown in colour, will be found on

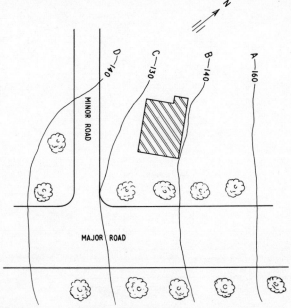

Fig. 11.1. Contour lines

ordnance survey maps and will contain numerals. By tracing along a selected contour line it will be seen that the numeral remains the same, which is an indication that the surface represented by the numeral is a given height above ordnance datum.

107

Plans of large site works will also contain contour lines and while
these may have more detail the purpose is the same (Fig. 11.1).

The site plan in this case shows a major road, a minor road, a
building and agricultural land. In this case the contour lines are
lettered A, B, C and D and each contains a number indicating the
height above ordnance datum.

On inspection it will be seen that A to B has a fall of 20 ft, B to C
has a fall of 10 ft and C to D has a rise of 10 ft. From this we are
able to see that within the area of the contour line C the land forms a
valley. By tracing lines D and C to where they pass across the minor
highway we see that the highway rises from the intersection to the
contour line D. By tracing each line to where it passes across the
major highway we see that this highway has a difference in level of

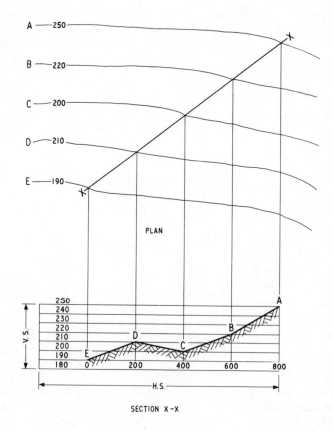

SECTION X–X

Fig. 11.2. Developing contour lines

40 ft between A and D but a valley exists adjacent to the contour line C which indicates that the highway has a gradient from contour line D falling to the intersection and then a rising gradient from the intersection to contour line A.

By studying contour lines on maps and plans it is possible to determine the rise or fall of the land and when scales have been used it is possible to determine the rate of rise or fall or more correctly the gradient.

11.1 SECTIONS

When greater detail is required about the contours, sectional drawings would be produced using a horizontal scale for the linear measurement of the land and a vertical scale to indicate the variation in levels. It is not uncommon to use a vertical scale ten times larger than the horizontal scale (Fig. 11.2).

If the horizontal scale is 1 in. = 100 ft the vertical scale would be 1 in. = 10 ft but these must not be considered as standard scales.

To draw a section of the contours through a line X–X, each of the contour lines A, B, C, D and E, where they are cut by X–X, are drawn as vertical lines from the plan.

The horizontal scale now represents the cut X–X and the vertical scale the height of the contour lines.

The vertical scale is now marked off where it coincides with the horizontal scale and reproduced as shown in the section. From this it is possible to ascertain the shape of the surface represented by the contour lines.

11.2 GRID LINES

Most construction works will require some excavation to be carried out and in many cases a proportion of fill will also be required. To determine the cut and fill necessary on a site a clear indication of the levels must be known.

By using a system of grid lines and establishing levels it is possible to obtain a reasonable assessment of the site.

The grid lines consist of a series of carefully set out pegs representing a grid system set off a base line that can be tied to a feature or a drawing.

The base line may consist of a straight fence, line of telegraph poles, edge of carriageway or a line set out by means of ranging poles, providing it is tied to a feature.

Assume a site adjacent to a straight section of highway is to be used and the edge of the carriageway used as the base line (Fig. 11.3). The grid lines are to be set out by means of a chain or steel band to form squares, with each side measuring 100 ft in length.

Commencing at grid line A, each of the positions B, C, D, E and

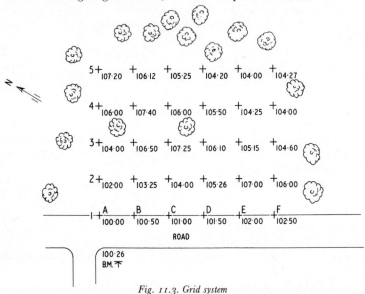

Fig. 11.3. Grid system

F are established at the edge of the carriageway as a straight line.

The lines are then set out at right-angles to the edge of the carriageway and each 100 ft established on the site by means of a wooden peg, ranging pole or steel arrow.

When carrying out this task it is important that extra care be taken in establishing accurate right-angles; any deviation from accuracy will result in an irregular grid system.

The points of intersection in this case will be A1, A2, A3, A4 and A5, followed by B1, B2, B3, B4 and B5 until all points are established on the site.

The bench mark shown as 100·26 is now used to establish the reduced levels at each of the points on the grid using a levelling instrument and a levelling staff.

While inspection of the grid system will indicate the rise and fall of the land, a number of sections can be produced from it and will indicate the true shape of the site.

By producing sections of the site it will be possible to estimate the volume of cut and fill that will be required.

Chapter 12

THE COWLEY AUTOMATIC LEVEL

While it is often the practice to use boning rods or straight-edge and spirit-level on sites to obtain levels or heights over short distances, the Cowley automatic level which has an accuracy of $\frac{1}{4}$ in. at 100 ft may be used.

The instrument consists of a box $4\frac{3}{4}$ in. by $5\frac{1}{2}$ in. by 2 in. and weighs $2\frac{3}{4}$ lb (Fig. 12.1).

The instrument is used on a metal tripod 38 in. high in conjunction with a staff which is graduated on the rear side and which contains a movable horizontal target bar (Fig. 12.2).

The body of the instrument consists of two solidly constructed aluminium die-castings. In the narrow front portion is a viewing aperture and on the top an eyepiece. Inside the case is a unique system of mirrors one of which is mounted on a pendulum which is delicately yet robustly pivoted. All working parts are enclosed and there are no knobs, screws or controls to manipulate.

The tripod has a vertical pin on which the instrument is mounted by means of a small hole in the instrument casing at the bottom rear corner.

The action of placing the instrument on the pin releases a clamp locking the pendulum and the instrument is then ready for use.

12.1 THE THEORY OF THE MIRROR SYSTEM

The Cowley automatic level is based on light rays which will rebound from a flat ground mirrored surface at exactly the same angle from which they entered.

In the left-hand system light is reflected in turn from two fixed

111

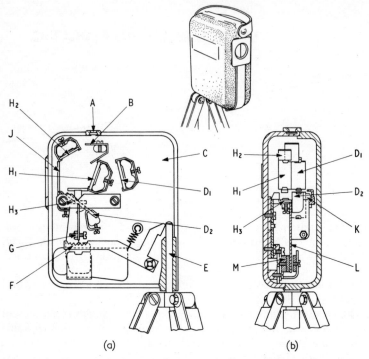

Fig. *12.1. Cowley automatic level: (a) side view; (b) front view*

A	*eyepiece*	H_1	*1st mirror, right-hand system*
B	*mask*	H_2	*2nd mirror, right-hand system*
C	*optical centre*	H_3	*3rd mirror, right-hand system*
D_1	*1st mirror, left-hand system*	J	*Image division bar*
D_2	*2nd mirror, left-hand system*	K	*Knife edges*
E	*Tripod peg*	L	*Pendulum*
F	*Pendulum clamp*	M	*Magnet*
G	*Pendulum balance adjusting screw*		

mirrors. This system has the feature possessed by the optical square which is used for surveying [Fig. 12.3(a)].

The direction in which the light leaves the second mirror always makes the same angle with the entering ray [Fig. 12.3(b)].

In the right-hand system the first two mirrors are fixed and the third is mounted on a pendulum and is therefore always horizontal [Fig. 12.3(c)].

Light always leaves the second mirror, making a constant angle with the entering ray. It then strikes the third mirror which being always horizontal, reflects the light in a direction which is still constant with respect to the entering ray [Fig. 12.3(d)].

When viewing objects in the horizontal datum plane defined by the instrument, they appear in the same position in either the left- or right-hand system, and the effect of coincidence is observed when the Cowley automatic level, staff and target are used.

If the target bar is lowered so that it is below the datum plane, it will appear lower in the left-hand view, but since the right-hand

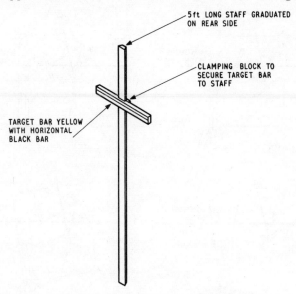

5 ft LONG STAFF GRADUATED
ON REAR SIDE

CLAMPING BLOCK TO
SECURE TARGET BAR
TO STAFF

TARGET BAR YELLOW
WITH HORIZONTAL
BLACK BAR

Fig. 12.2. Target bar used with Cowley level

view is inverted it will appear higher in that and the bar will not appear continuous [Fig. 12.4(a), (b)]. If the target bar is above the datum plane the reverse happens.

When the instrument is tilted forwards or backwards the two semi-circular fields of view become displaced up and down, but the position of coincidence is unaffected [Fig. 12.4(c)].

If the instrument is tilted to the left or right the bar appears inclined in opposite directions in each half. The position of coincidence is once more unaffected [Fig. 12.4 (d)].

An essential feature of the Cowley automatic level optical design is that the datum horizontal plane passes through a point C, on the vertical axis, about which the instrument rotates on the tripod and this point C is the image of a point P on the knife edge supporting the pendulum mirror after reflection in reverse order by either reflecting system.

Thus C may be called the optical centre of the instrument and because it is in this position errors in level of the instrument have no effect upon the results given by it.

In theory, the fixed mirrors should be exactly at right-angles to the central plane and each pair with exactly the same included angle.

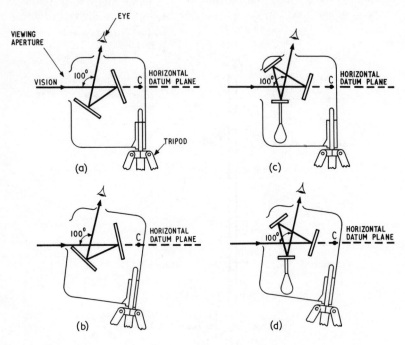

Fig. 12.3. The mirror system

The gravitationally controlled mirror should also be pivoted on an axis lying on its own plane of reflection, and normal to the central plane.

Any or all the mirrors might be adjustable to effect this relationship, but in practice the fixed mirrors are mounted on supports machined flat at right-angles to the base of the holding jig and at correct angles, to ordinary engineering accuracy, and any errors in levelling are corrected by adjusting the hang of the controlling pendulum using the adjustable balance screw with locknut.

Any errors in the correct setting of the mirrors at right-angles to the central plane are automatically compensated in the adjustment of the alignment of the pivotal axis of the gravitationally controlled mirror.

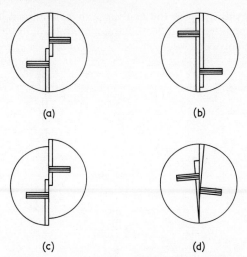

(a)   (b)

(c)   (d)

Fig. 12.4. (a), (b) Views of target bar lower than datum plane when horizontal; (c) view of target bar when instrument is tilted; (d) view of target bar when instrument is not horizontal

12.2 USING THE COWLEY AUTOMATIC LEVEL

The tripod is opened to allow the pin on the head to be uppermost. The Cowley level is placed so that the aperture on the base is engaged with the pin. The instrument is now ready for use.

If the instrument appears tilted it is best to set it as near horizontal as possible, although this will not affect the efficiency of the levelling.

The target bar is held at a predetermined position and the instrument directed to the target bar.

The observer looks through the eyepiece in the top of the instrument. By means of two mirror systems in the instrument, two views of the target bar will be seen, one on the left and one on the right.

The observer signals to the assistant holding the staff to move the target bar up or down as the case may be until the two halves are brought into coincidence (Fig. 12.5).

The first view obtained when looking through the eyepiece may be any one of those shown in Fig. 12.4.

The views seen as C and D would mean that the instrument is not horizontal but even so this would not prevent coincidence from being obtained as shown in Fig. 12.5.

When the assistant has been informed by signals that the target bar is correct, he should secure it to the staff by means of the screw positioned at the rear.

Other levels equal to the first one can be obtained by swivelling the instrument to any angle, moving the target and sighting through the instrument (Fig. 12.6).

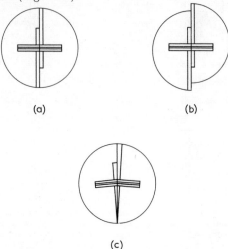

(a)   (b)

(c)

Fig. 12.5. (a) View of target bar adjusted to datum plane;
(b) view of target bar adjusted to datum plane when
instrument is tilted; (c) view of target bar adjusted to
datum plane when instrument is not horizontal

If A is the first level peg and B is to be the second peg, the target is held on peg A and coincidence obtained, the target is moved to peg B and this peg driven into the ground until coincidence is obtained.

12.3 VARIATION IN LEVELS

When it is necessary to fix pegs at plus or minus in relation to a datum (Fig. 12.7).

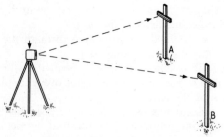

Fig. 12.6. Using the Cowley level

Assume a view is taken at the datum A and the target bar is found to be fixed at 3 ft. Peg B is to be 1 ft lower than A. Fix the target bar at 4 ft, hold the staff at B, swivel the instrument and sight on to the target bar. Drive peg B into the ground until coincidence is obtained.

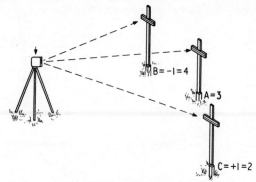

Fig. 12.7. Setting levels with the Cowley level

Peg C is to be 1 ft higher than A, fix the target bar at 2 ft, hold the staff at C, swivel the instrument to sight on to the target bar, drive peg C into the ground until coincidence is obtained.

12.4 ESTABLISHING RISE AND FALL

A fitting called a slope attachment may be used with the Cowley automatic level and permits intermediate pegs to be produced for gradients.

The attachment is designed to fit over the object aperture of the instrument. It has a variable control for giving rise and fall of the instrument's horizontal line of sight, to suit gradients up to a maximum of 1 in 10.

Assume it is proposed to establish pegs for a gradient of 1 in 100 over a distance of 50 ft (Fig. 12.8).

With A as the datum, measure 50 ft to B and drive a peg into the ground. Set up the instrument at X. An assistant holds the staff with the target bar at A. Sight through the instrument and allow the assistant to adjust the target bar until coincident with the line of sight; assume the reading on the staff is seen to be 3 ft 6 in.

Now raise the target bar to 4 ft on the staff. The assistant holds the staff on peg B, a sight is taken through the instrument and peg B is adjusted until the image is coincident with the line of sight.

The target bar is now lowered to 3 ft 6 in. and the staff is held on peg B (Fig. 12.9).

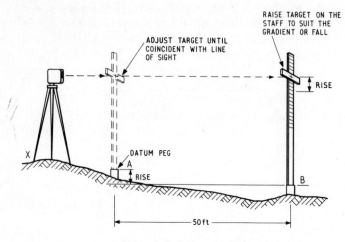

Fig. 12.8. Producing a gradient

With the attachment fixed to the Cowley automatic level, a sight is taken through the instrument until the image of the target bar is coincident.

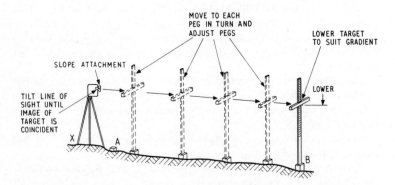

Fig. 12.9. Using the slope attachment

Pegs are now placed at 10 ft spacing between A and B, the staff is transferred to each peg in turn and the pegs adjusted so that the target image viewed through the instrument is coincident with the line of sight.

12.5 TESTING THE COWLEY AUTOMATIC LEVEL

When handled with reasonable care the Cowley level will remain accurate, but should it be knocked and testing of the instrument is considered advisable, this can be done on the site.

Mark out three places in line ACB, each 10 ft apart (Fig. 12.10).

Set up the Cowley level at C with an assistant holding the staff at A. Sight through the instrument and signal for the target bar

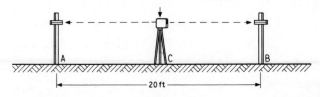

Fig. 12.10. Checking the Cowley level

to be moved until it is coincident with the line of sight. The target bar is secured and the reading on the rear of the staff recorded.

The staff is moved to position B, the instrument is swivelled and directed on to the staff. The target bar is adjusted until it is coincident with the line of sight. The target bar is secured and the reading recorded.

The difference between the readings A and B is noted.

From B measure 30 ft in line with AB and establish D (Fig. 12.11).

Move the Cowley level from C and set it up at D, swivel the instrument to sight on to A.

An assistant holds the staff at A. A sight is taken through the

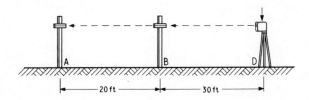

Fig. 12.11. Checking the Cowley level

instrument and the target bar adjusted until a reading is obtained and is recorded.

The staff is moved to position B, a sight is made through the instrument and the target bar adjusted until a reading is obtained and is recorded.

If the procedure is carried out with care, the difference in the

readings AB from C and AB from D should not exceed $\frac{1}{8}$ in. When
the difference in readings exceeds this the instrument requires adjusting.

If the readings taken from C are found to be:

$$A = 2 \text{ ft } 10 \text{ in.}$$
$$B = 2 \text{ ft } 8 \text{ in.}$$
$$\text{difference} = \underline{\qquad 2 \text{ in.}}$$

and the readings taken from D are found to be:

$$A = 3 \text{ ft } 1\tfrac{1}{2} \text{ in.}$$
$$B = 2 \text{ ft } 11\tfrac{1}{2} \text{ in.}$$
$$\text{difference} = \underline{\qquad 2 \text{ in.}}$$

the instrument is correct.

If readings taken from C are found to be:

$$A = 2 \text{ ft } 10 \text{ in.}$$
$$B = 2 \text{ ft } 8 \text{ in.}$$
$$\text{difference} = \underline{\qquad 2 \text{ in.}}$$

and the reading taken from D are found to be:

$$A = 3 \text{ ft } 1\tfrac{1}{2} \text{ in.}$$
$$B = 2 \text{ ft } 11 \text{ in.}$$
$$\text{difference} = \underline{\qquad 2\tfrac{1}{2} \text{ in.}}$$

the instrument requires adjusting.

Chapter 13

THE SITESQUARE

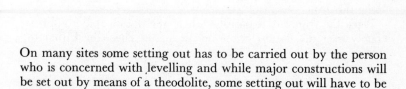

On many sites some setting out has to be carried out by the person who is concerned with levelling and while major constructions will be set out by means of a theodolite, some setting out will have to be carried out by other means.

The sitesquare has been designed for setting out straight lines and offset lines at 90°. The instrument consists of a cylindrical metal case

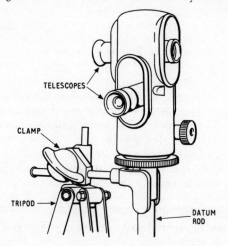

TELESCOPES

CLAMP

TRIPOD

DATUM ROD

Fig. 13.1. The sitesquare

containing two telescopes, a fine setting screw near the base, a circular spirit-level on the top and a knurled ring at the base (**Fig.** 13.1).

The sitesquare is used together with a datum rod screwed into the base of the instrument and which contains a spiked extension at the bottom capable of being secured to the datum rod. A clamp arm is used to fix the instrument to a steel pin set on the top of a metal tripod and secured by means of a clamp screw.

13.1 SETTING UP THE SITESQUARE

The sitesquare is used to set out lines at right-angles from a known datum.

The tripod is set up so that the steel pin is uppermost. Place the clamp of the datum arm over the tripod pin and position the arm so that it is nearly horizontal, with the clamp about mid-distance along the arm.

Place the tripod in a position where the datum rod is approximately over the datum peg which is on the site. Check that the

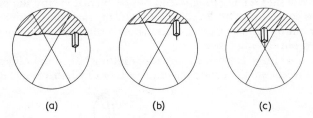

(a)   (b)   (c)

Fig. 13.2. Views when using the sitesquare: (a) first view; (b) manipulating the fine setting screw; (c) obtaining the correct view

tripod legs are firmly set on the ground. The extended spike at the lower end of the datum rod has a point at one end and a hollow at the other end. The pointed end is set on a datum mark on the peg or if a nail has been inserted into the top of the peg the hollow end of the spike is used to set upon the head of the nail.

Release the spike screw and extend the spike until it rests firmly on the datum and then secure the spike screw.

Place the sitesquare on top of the datum rod and secure the instrument by turning the knurled ring in a clockwise direction. This secures the sitesquare on to the datum rod but permits the instrument to be rotated.

Having set up the instrument take a look at the circular bubble; if this appears 'off centre' hold the instrument with one hand and release the clamp screw. The instrument is then moved slightly until the bubble is in the centre of the black ring on the glass. The clamp screw is then made secure, the bubble checked again and the instrument is ready for use.

13.2 IMAGE SEEN THROUGH A SITESQUARE

When care has been taken in setting up the sitesquare the object seen through the telescope will be vertical and will cut the intersection of the cross-lines in the lens (Fig. 13.2).

The sitesquare is set up with the datum rod on the datum peg

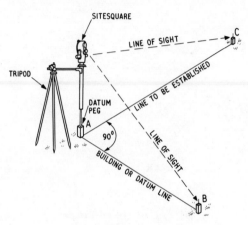

Fig. 13.3. Setting out a right-angle

and the instrument is rotated so that one telescope is on the base line A–B (Fig. 13.3).

The instrument is locked in position and the telescope sighted on to B by adjusting the fine setting screw. When sighting on to peg B the actual datum may be a mark or a nail which must be central to the cross-lines for the alignment to be accurate.

13.3 SETTING OUT A RIGHT-ANGLE

Once the instrument has been set up and the first telescope sighted on to peg B, the instrument must not be moved. A sight is now made through the second telescope and a ranging pole or a wooden peg held as near as possible at right-angles to line AB.

The observer signals for the ranging pole to be moved until it is in view. To obtain the exact position, insert a wooden peg in the ground. A pencil is held on top of the peg and 'sighted in'; a pencil mark is made on the peg at the exact position.

If it is required to set out a square or rectangle (Fig. 13.4).

The sitesquare is moved from datum peg A and set up with the spike of the datum rod on the mark on peg C.

One telescope is sighted on to peg A and peg D is established by sighting through the second telescope.

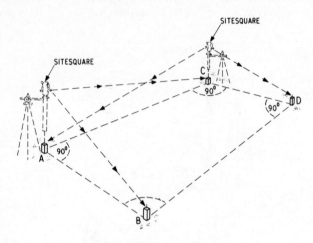

Fig. 13.4. Setting out a rectangle

Chapter 14

CARE AND ADJUSTMENT OF INSTRUMENTS

14.1 CARE OF INSTRUMENTS

Equipment and instruments used for levelling and setting out must be considered as fragile and should at all times be treated with care. This applies particularly where instruments have to be stored and used on construction sites.

Measuring tapes, which are so necessary on sites, must be wiped clean and kept dry, or when wet they should be opened out to full length to dry at the first opportunity. Steel tapes, bands and chains must always be wiped clean once they have been used on a site.

Tripods should be examined periodically to make certain that straps and screws are secure. The head of the tripod must be kept clean and free from grit. Tripods must be wiped dry before being stored after use. A high standard practised in the care of tripods and similar equipment can result in many years of freedom from maintenance.

Although levelling should be carried out during periods of rain-free weather, sometimes it is necessary to continue using instruments during a shower of rain.

When rain is forecast, a piece of polythene sheeting or similar waterproof material should be placed over the instrument as protection during its use.

Instruments that do come into contact with water must be wiped dry at the first opportunity and for this a soft cloth is most suitable, although in an emergency a paper handkerchief will suffice. A second wiping must follow, however, because fibres from the paper, if used too often, can foul the movable parts of an instrument.

The external surface of the object glass and the lens of the eyepiece should be wiped dry. A very small amount of light instrument

125

oil may be applied to screw threads and a ball joint but the surface concerned must be wiped free from excess oil.

Care must be exercised when removing instruments from their cases and when replacing them. Cases are designed to secure instruments in particular positions which must be known before removing an instrument from its container.

Levelling staffs must not be overlooked in the care of equipment. The staff, whether made from wood or metal, must be wiped dry and clean after use. When the scale on the face of a staff becomes dirty it may be cleaned with warm water and a soft cloth.

If a scale is of linen secured to the staff make certain that the bond between linen and staff has not become brittle to the extent that the linen is peeling at the edges.

14.2 ADJUSTMENT OF INSTRUMENTS

To enable levelling instruments to give the required efficiency, it is necessary to check them at intervals, particularly when more than one person on a site is concerned with using them.

Temporary adjustments can be made on a site but when it is

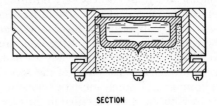

SECTION

Fig. 14.1. Mounting the circular bubble

found that this is insufficient to correct errors and a permanent adjustment is required, the instrument should be returned to the supplier or instrument maker.

14.2.1 ADJUSTING A CIRCULAR BUBBLE

The levelling instrument is placed on the tripod head and adjusted until the circular bubble is central. The head of the instrument is unclamped and rotated 180°. If the bubble does not remain central some adjustment is required.

On the underside of the bubble case will be found four screws. Two opposite screws clamp the case to the body of the instrument and the other two have an antagonistic action (Fig. 14.1).

These screws must be used in pairs by slightly loosening one and tightening the one opposite to it. This will cause the bubble to move along a line joining the screws. The correct pair of screws must be selected according to the direction the bubble is decentred. Correct half the bubble displacement by the screws; the bubble should then be brought central by the quick-levelling head. Repeat the operation until the bubble remains central. Make certain that all the screws are tight.

14.2.2 ADJUSTING THE DUMPY LEVEL

Adjustments may be temporary or permanent and while temporary adjustment can be carried out on a site it would be necessary to have instruments for carrying out permanent adjustments.

It is the author's opinion that readers should not attempt any permanent adjustments until they are familiar with levelling instruments. Major adjustments and replacements should be carried out by instrument makers.

Temporary adjustments are carried out by setting up the dumpy level and adjusting the telescope by using the levelling foot screws

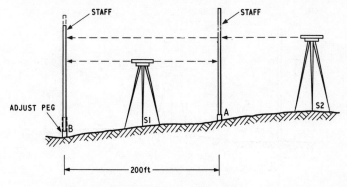

Fig. 14.2. Checking a dumpy level

until the line of sight or observed line, when viewed through the telescope, is parallel to the axis of the bubble-tube, which would enable all observations to be made on the same horizontal plane.

Focusing the lenses correctly is a temporary adjustment, and to produce a good focus to suit the observer's eyesight requires the manipulation of the eyepiece and the focusing screw so that the image of the object being observed is seen as clearly as possible. If parallax is found when sighting through the telescope, it must be eliminated.

Permanent adjustment involves altering the bubble-tube so that the bubble remains in the centre of its run and adjusting the line of collimation. To adjust the bubble, set up the dumpy level making certain the tripod is firm.

Place the telescope over two of the levelling foot screws and adjust the screws until the bubble is central. Rotate the telescope 180°. If the bubble has moved out of centre, eliminate half the error by moving the foot screws and the other half by means of the capstan-headed screws located at the ends. Set the telescope at 90° to the first position and repeat any necessary adjustment. The bubble should now remain central.

The line of collimation may be adjusted by using a two-peg method (Fig. 14.2).

Select a level site and insert the ground pegs A and B, 200 ft apart. Set up the dumpy level at S1, mid-distance between A and B. Level the telescope making certain that the bubble remains in the centre of its run. Take a reading on a levelling staff held at A. Move the levelling staff to peg B and adjust this peg until the same reading is obtained on the staff when a sight is taken from S1.

The dumpy level is now moved to position S2, any reasonable

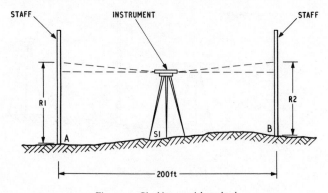

Fig. 14.3. Checking a quick-set level

distance from A and in line with AB, so that a sighting can be made on a levelling staff held at A and B.

The levelling staff is held on peg A and a reading obtained, the staff is moved to B and a reading obtained. If the readings are the same the line of collimation is correct.

If the readings are not the same the line of collimation requires adjusting. This is done by moving the diaphragm up or down slightly by manipulation of the capstan-headed screws until the collimation is found to have been adjusted.

14.2.3 CHECKING AND ADJUSTING THE QUICK-SET LEVEL

Select a reasonably level site about 200 ft long and allow for a levelling staff to be held at A and B, each end of the site, with the instrument set up at S1 mid-distance between A and B (Fig. 14.3).

Direct the telescope to the staff at A, level the telescope and take a reading R1. Rotate the instrument and direct it to the staff at B and take a reading R2.

The difference in height between A and B, irrespective of any errors in the instrument, is $h_1 = R_1 - R_2$.

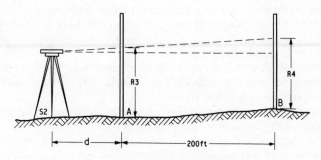

Fig. 14.4. Checking a quick-set level

Move the levelling instrument to position S2 at a distance $d = 20$ ft beyond A and in line with AB (Fig. 14.4).

Set up the instrument and level the telescope, direct the telescope on to the staff at A and take a reading R_3, and then take a reading R_4 on the staff at B.

The apparent difference in height between A and B is $h_2 = R_3 - R_4$.

The error is the measurement of the height difference between A and B expressed as:

$$\Delta h = h_2 - h_1 = (R_3 - R_4) - (R_1 - R_2)$$

Calculate:

$$R_4 + \Delta h \frac{(d+D)}{D}$$

taking care to treat the signs of the various quantities in a strictly algebraic manner.

The above calculation gives the staff reading at B which will be obtained when the line of sight of the telescope is horizontal.

To adjust the quick-set level, tilt the telescope using the tilting screw until the correct reading for R_4 is obtained, and then without moving the telescope adjust the bubble until it is in the centre of its run.

If the bubble is towards the object glass, slacken the upper of the two adjusting nuts which are visible through the corner of the bubble box and then adjust the lower nut upwards.

It is important to tighten the two nuts sufficiently to prevent them moving when the instrument is being carried. It is equally important to avoid tightening.

Also ensure that the small screw visible in the hole at the end of the bubble box is tight.

The method for checking the autoset levels is identical to that for quick-set levels, except that the autoset levels have no bubble to centre, apart from the small circular bubble which ensures that the stabiliser is within its range of operation.

If the instrument is found to be in error it may be corrected by adjusting the graticule adjusting screw which is exposed when the breech end cover is removed.

If the collimation error is large it may be necessary to adjust the position of the balance weights on the pendulum.

It is the author's opinion, as previously stated, that permanent adjustments of any nature should be carried out by the instrument makers and adjustments on the site should be of a temporary nature.

14.2.4 ADJUSTMENT OF LEVELLING SCREWS

The movement of the levelling screws should be reasonably firm, not stiff and not too loose. Sometimes a thread may have been stripped, in which case a new adjusting screw is required.

The tension of the screws on an autoset level can be increased by turning the wear adjusting screws, and the hexagonal bolts which clamp the retaining plate of the levelling screw ball feet can also be tightened to take up any slackness.

14.2.5 SQUARING THE GRATICULE

This adjustment requires the use of special tools and should be carried out by the instrument maker. An attempt to square the graticule on a site by an unqualified person can result in disturbing the mounting.

14.3 CLEANING THE INSTRUMENT

Sometimes, and particularly after an instrument has been used on a site during periods of rain, it is found necessary to attempt cleaning.

Extreme care must be taken at all times and cleaning should be carried out on a sheet of white paper placed on a flat surface.

The makers' instructions should be adhered to for cleaning because of the variation in design of certain instruments.

Normally the object glass can be wiped clean with a soft cloth. The eyepiece lens can also be cleaned without removal apart from unscrewing it from the telescope. The surface of the diaphragm glass can similarly be cleaned, care being taken not to wipe away the web lines.

After cleaning, all lenses must be polished and all parts that have been removed must be replaced correctly.

The application of a precision instrument lubricant is suitable for threads and ball joints, provided that excess lubricant which could attract dust is removed.

INDEX